THE PAST IN THE PRESENT

General Editor: Jacquetta Hawkes

LIVING FOSSILS

MAURICE BURTON D.Sc.

Living Fossils

WITH EIGHTY-THREE DRAWINGS

BY JANE BURTON

THAMES AND HUDSON

LONDON · NEW YORK

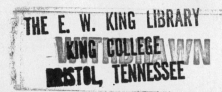

CONTENTS

v

ILLUSTRATIONS

ACKNOWLEDGMENTS

The author takes this opportunity to express his indebtedness to the British Museum (Natural History) for specimens exhibited in their galleries; to the authors of numerous scientific papers and books consulted, to the colleagues who have helped with advice, and to the publishers for the care taken in handling the manuscript presented to them.

Due acknowledgment is also made to the undermentioned for kind permission to quote certain passages appearing on the pages indicated: *Illustrated London News*, 68, 136, 138, 236; the Trustees, British Museum (Natural History), 174, 240 from *Succession of Life*; *Australian Journal of Science*, 156; the Ray Society, London, 153; Carl G. Hartman, University of Texas, *Possums*, 77, 78; *The Standard Natural History* (Frederick Warne & Co.), 173; W. P. Pycraft, *History of Birds* (Methuen & Co.), 201–202; W. T. Calman, *Life of the Crustacea* (Methuen & Co.), 134.

It may not be out of place to thank my daughter, Jane, for the amount of work put into the illustrating. Where possible her drawings have been made from actual specimens, but for many it has been necessary to adapt or modify illustrations in previous works, and acknowledgment is made to: the Trustees, British Museum (Natural History), 1–4, 45, 47 from *Succession of Life*, 5, 11, 13 from their galleries; *Illustrated London News*, 12, 20, 71; W. P. C. Tenison, *History of Fishes* (Norman), 67, 68, 69, 70, 72; R. E. Snodgrass, *Smithsonian Miscellaneous Collections*, 24, 27, 28, 46, 51; D. J. Scourfield, *Proceedings Linnean Society*, 49; W. T. Calman, *Life of the Crustacea*, 55; J. W. Evans, *Proceedings Royal Entomological Society*, 61; F. M. Carpenter, *American Journal of Science*, 58; E. I. White, *Discovery*, 73; G. G. Simpson, *Horses*, 79; R. J. Tillyard, *American Journal of Science*, 57; F. E. Zeuner, *Discovery*, 74; Neave Parker, *Oryx*, 83.

Vertebrates
- Mammals
- Birds
- Reptiles
- Amphibia
- Fishes
- Protochordata — Lancelets, Sea-squirts, etc.

Invertebrates

Arthropoda
- Spiders — King-crabs
- Xiphosura
- Insects
- Diplura
- Protura
- Collembola
- Crustacea
- Chilopoda — Centipedes
- Symphyla
- Diplopoda — Millipedes
- Prototracheata — Peripatus

- Mollusca
- Polyzoa
- Brachiopoda — Lamp-shells
- Annelida — Earthworms and marine Bristle Worms
- ("Worms") — (Omnibus title for parasitic worms, round worms, etc.)
- Echinoderma — Starfishes, sea-urchins
- Coelenterata — Jellyfishes, sea-anemones, corals
- Porifera — Sponges
- Protozoa — Unicellular animals

(This is not intended as a comprehensive table but is designed to show the general plan upon which discussions in this book are based.)

AGE IN MILLIONS OF YEARS		GEOLOGICAL PERIODS	SEAWEEDS	INVERTEBRATES	FISHES	LAND PLANTS	AMPHIBIA	REPTILES	BIRDS	MAMMALS
15	TERTIARY	PLIOCENE								
35		MIOCENE								
43		OLIGOCENE								
75		EOCENE								
140	MESOZOIC	CRETACEOUS								
170		JURASSIC								
195		TRIASSIC								
220	PALEOZOIC	PERMIAN								
275		CARBONI- FEROUS								
320		DEVONIAN								
350		SILURIAN								
420		ORDOVICIAN								
520	ARCHAEAN	CAMBRIAN								
? 1000		PRE- CAMBRIAN								

(The vast period of the Pre-Cambrian is represented by a foreshortened space at the base; at the top the small blank space represents the last million years, of the Pleistocene and Holocene (= most recent 10,000 years).)

INTRODUCTION

THE idea of ancient forms of life surviving on earth appeals to everyone. The excitement aroused by the capture of a fish believed long extinct, and by rumours of dinosaurs, monsters and serpents lurking in remote regions of the planet, the lasting popularity of Conan Doyle's *Lost World*, are all proof of this powerful attraction exercised by living fossils. Interesting survivors from the past are not in fact by any means all remote, rare—or fabulous. The human mind tends, however, to be more readily excited by the vague but romantic, if fictitious, than drawn to the solid fact. This has its advantages, for, if nothing else, it stimulates and maintains the search for novelties, and so leads to fresh discoveries. More often, the really instructive living fossil is some very familiar animal, or one whose description lies buried in the arid depths of a text-book.

In one sense, everything living today is a living fossil, in so far as it is a survivor from the past. Properly speaking, however, a living fossil is a plant or an animal that has survived beyond its era, although, as we shall see, its definition is not as clear-cut as this. It is the one species, or small group of species, that has continued in being when the many other closely related species have become extinct.

The lives of species, like those of individuals, vary in length and in what is accomplished during them. The fossil record is, in some places, now sufficiently complete for the histories of some species or families to be plotted in detail. These may be of two kinds. On the one hand, we have species which, from inconspicuous beginnings, in a few million years overrun the earth so that their fossil remains are widely found and in large numbers. Having reached a peak, in both distribution and populations, their demise is seen to be as rapid as their rise. On the other hand, there are species which appear to have increased slowly in numbers and in the extension of their range. They too have reached a peak, have taken longer to do so, and then their numbers slowly diminished, as did the area of the territory they occupied. The first may be said to have a short life but a gay one. Those of the second category may be likened to the slow plodders who accomplish nothing spectacular but persist over a longer period. It is they, especially, that have bequeathed to us the majority, if not all, of those plant and animal forms we call living fossils.

To label these two classes in this manner may be graphic, but it tells us nothing of the reasons why some are long-lived and others short-lived. What, then, are the causes of survival? To try to expound these is almost as unsatisfactory as are press interviews of centenarians. One attributes his long life to the fact that he has always had a pint of beer a day; another will ascribe it to total abstinence from all intoxicating liquor. A third will attribute his long life to the fact that he has always smoked like a chimney, a fourth to the total abstinence from tobacco, and so on. So with the survival of species, the causes are uncertain and vary with the species.

Interest in living fossils, for the scientist, lies mainly in the light they may shed on unsolved problems. To the layman, and for that matter the scientist also, there is always lurking in the background the possibility—even perhaps the hope—that some spectacular discovery, in the seas, in remote lakes or inaccessible reaches of large rivers, or even in uncharted parts of the land, may reveal survivors of the past. Speculations on this possibility have little value except in relation to what is already known of living fossils, or missing links, so-called. The main text of this book is, therefore, devoted primarily to what is known of living fossils, and secondarily to what can be reasonably included as scientific speculation as to the causes of long-continued survival. Finally, as a kind of interpolated appendix, some space is devoted to the "mystery" animals of today and the chances, however remote, of future surprises of this sort in the biological field.

In writing this book, I have relied for my information on scientific literature, examination of specimens in the public galleries of the British Museum (Natural History) and the advice given me by friends and colleagues where necessary. In the interpretation of the facts, however, I have accepted orthodox views only where they seem to me convincing, and have not hesitated to try wherever possible a new point of view. I can only hope that in writing the text I have made it sufficiently clear where the opinions or speculations are my own.

To deal exhaustively with the subject of living fossils would entail the analysis and documentation of almost all that is known of geology and biology. Even with the generous help received, this would be an impossible task; the alternative is to select such salient features as will give a general understanding and no more. So it follows that, as a mere matter of convenience, and as an aid to the total understanding, it may be necessary to give the greater emphasis to the living animals in one instance, to the fossil remains in another, and so on.

In seeking to reconstruct the pedigree of the larger groups of organisms—and this we must do in studying living fossils— we have three main lines of evidence to draw upon. First, there is the study of comparative anatomy which enables us with some degree of confidence to determine the relationship between organisms or groups of organisms. This is especially useful in dealing with those now living, but its results can also be applied to those long dead. Then we have the study of life-histories, which, if they do not always recapitulate the history of the race, as was formerly believed, nevertheless contain valuable clues. Finally, we have the study of fossil remains to give the order of succession in time. By it we can trace the forerunners if not the actual ancestors of living species. Unfortunately, only a small proportion of the total number of organisms that have lived in the past is available to us. There are therefore many gaps.

In these days of vast accumulations of knowledge and of specialist studies, anyone attempting to collate information over a wide field is in the position of being himself, for the time being, little more than an informed layman. While this has its drawbacks it has, in this instance, perhaps, one advantage. Doubtless, to those thoroughly immersed in the subject, the assessment of geological time is relatively easy. One who studies, primarily, the living animal, needs to be constantly reminding himself that the Devonian period, say, began 320 million years ago and ended 275 million years ago. It has therefore been assumed that the majority reading this book will be in similar case, and if there is the appearance of mentioning such figures too often, it is because of the hope that such reiteration will not only serve as a guide, but will keep constantly to the forefront the immense periods of time involved.

That the present can only be understood in relation to the past is, by its very nature, especially true of living fossils. But while it would be outside the scope of this work to deal in any detail with the changes that have taken place on the earth in the last 500 million years or more, a brief outline of these changes is essential. It is only by such a survey, for example, that we can appreciate why Australia and New Zealand should be the home of so many archaic survivors, why the outstanding survivors of New Zealand should be a frog, a reptile and a bird, and those of Australia should be archaic mammals. And why the living fossils found on land should be so largely concentrated in Australia, South Africa and South and Central America. The appreciation of these things lies largely in our knowledge of the changes in the landmasses and of their climates. More especially is it a *sine quâ non* of the study of the phylogeny of insects and of the primitive members of that vast group.

It is now generally accepted that life originated on this earth more than 1,000 million years ago. Some writers put it at

1,500 million. During the first 1,000 million years or so, in
what is called the Pre-Cambrian period, vast changes took
place in the nature of the earth's surface. The barren deserts
and mountains, with their volcanoes and steaming lava fields
which characterised the land-masses, underwent tremendous
and far-reaching movements. The older mountain ranges were
worn down while elsewhere new ranges were thrown up. The
climate, too, fluctuated, for even the Pre-Cambrian had its
ice ages. And from this enormous period in the earth's history
little remains to tell us of the living organisms. The fossils found
in the rocks of the later stages of the Pre-Cambrian period are
few and difficult to interpret. They include imprints of jellyfish,
the remains of horny lamp-shells and evidence of the activity
of worms rather than of the worms themselves, together with
impressions of the half-worm, half-insect, *Xenusion*, to be
discussed later. Yet, in the earliest rocks of the succeeding
period, the Cambrian, traces of a considerable variety of
invertebrates have been found. From this, it may be assumed
that a wide variety of plants and animals had lived and died
during at least a large part of the Pre-Cambrian, and that their
remains had been irrevocably destroyed.

At the opening of the Cambrian period, 520 million years
ago, there was one main land-mass, which geologists have
called Gondwanaland. This continent extended from South
America to what is now the continent of Africa and eastwards
to the south-western corner of Australia (*see* fig. 1). In addition
to Gondwanaland there were a number of smaller land-masses
including one covering most of North America and the
western half of Greenland, which in its later stages is known as
the continent of Laurentia. The weather was probably mainly
equable during the Cambrian period, although there were
some deserts. However, the fossils remaining from this period
are entirely marine, so that little is known about conditions on
land. Towards the end of the period, it seems, the seas began
to recede, leaving large areas of the sea-floor as dry land. With
the opening of the Ordovician period, which commenced

420 million years ago, the seas began once again to encroach on the land. Incidentally, it may be noted that whereas the Cambrian contained a wealth of invertebrates it is during the Ordovician period, which continued for 70 million years, that the first recognisable vertebrates are found.

The 30 million years of the Silurian period that followed had, like the Ordovician, a mainly equable climate. New land areas slowly emerged during the Silurian and new mountain ranges were beginning to form. It is in the rocks of this period that the first land plants have been registered. At the close of the period, however, fresh volcanic activity accompanied by earth movements brought more land above sea-level. The 45 million years' duration of the Devonian period saw the land vegetation develop to lay the foundations of our modern flora. Wingless insects, together with forms similar to our present-day woodlice, millipedes, mites and spiders also appeared on land.

By the beginning of the Carboniferous period—that is, 275 million years ago—Gondwanaland had considerably extended its boundaries to include much more of what is now Australia, together with southern Asia and part of the North Atlantic. Concurrently, two smaller continents had been developing in the northern hemisphere and now occupied a considerable part of the seas to the north of Gondwanaland. The continent of Laurentia had extended its range from eastern North America across Greenland to northern and central Europe. In its south-western corner it became joined to Gondwanaland, although this junction did not last long. The other continent, Angara, covered what is now northern Asia. There were other smaller land-masses, but consideration of these three alone suffices to follow the isolation of the marsupials and monotremes, which will be dealt with in early chapters, and the development of the insects, which is the subject of later ones. The Carboniferous period and the Permian which followed it brings us to the end of the Primary or Paleozoic period, with no significant changes in the land-masses.

The ensuing Secondary or Mesozoic lasted for the next 150 million years. Beginning 195 million years ago, with the Triassic, it included also the Jurassic and Cretaceous periods. Towards its close the conifers and ferns were being superseded by the flowering plants as the dominant members of the land flora. During the Mesozoic the land animals became abundant, including many invertebrates as well as all the groups of vertebrates represented in our modern fauna. The reptiles reached their heyday in the Age of Reptiles, when the giant dinosaurs, as well as many other reptiles, large and small, dominated the scene. During it, also, Gondwanaland was breaking up to form four main masses, that to the west approximating to what we now recognise as South America, and a central mass which foreshadowed the present continent of Africa. Farther to the east, the continent of Australia and the islands of New Zealand were beginning to take shape, and to the south lay what is now known as Antarctica, which was joined at various times and in varying ways to the other three. There was also a smaller area to the east of the African mass which was formerly supposed to have stretched from Madagascar to the southern tip of the Indian peninsula, and which received the name of Lemuria. It is now believed that this never did reach to India and that its boundaries embraced little more than what is now known as Madagascar.

The supposed location and changes of the land-masses of the world are illustrated in the maps on pages 8-9, which carry the story over the next 75 million years or so, through the Eocene, Oligocene, Miocene and Pliocene, to the time when the continents and islands forming the land-masses as we know them today were taking on their present outlines and the final shaping of our modern flora and fauna was taking place. The maps are not necessarily correct in detail, and doubtless should be revised in the light of knowledge gained since they were first published. For example, the continent of Antarctica must have formed a more integral part of Gondwanaland than is suggested in them, while the several land-masses derived from

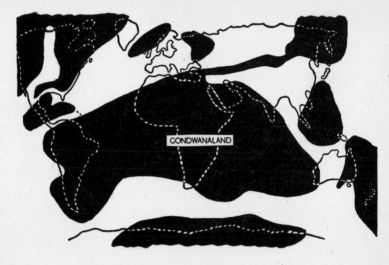

1. Geography of the Cambrian Period

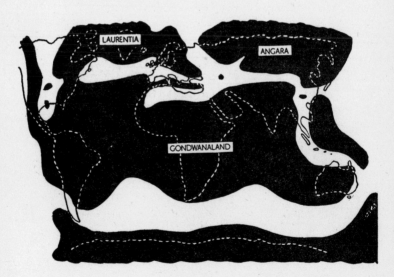

2. Geography of the Lower Carboniferous Period

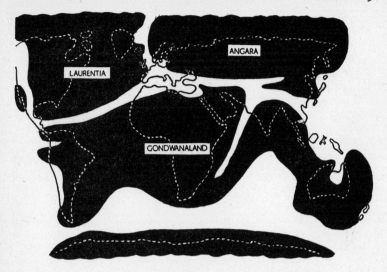

3. Geography of the Jurassic Period

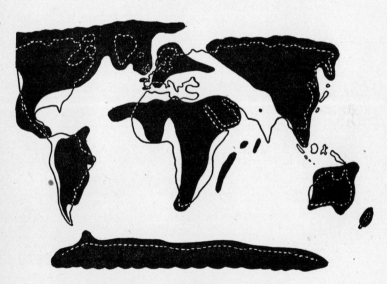

4. Geography of the Eocene Period

1-4. MAPS SHOWING CHANGES IN THE LAND-MASSES OF THE
WORLD in geological times, in relation to the present day.

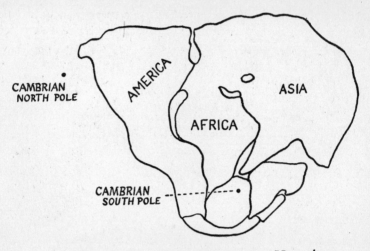

5. THEORY OF CONTINENTAL DRIFT. How the
continents can be fitted together: the starting point
for the theory.

the latter must have had connections with Antarctica at least
as late as the Cretaceous. The floras of Patagonia and New
Zealand are markedly similar and the living and fossil insects
from these two regions suggest that migrations took place from
Antarctica to New Zealand, Australia and South America
as late as the Cretaceous. It is probable also that the present
similarities in the marsupial faunas of Australia and South
America derive from migrations of early marsupials from
Antarctica northwards. Nevertheless, this series of maps forms
a useful starting point for a discussion.

For the sake of completeness mention should be made of
Wegener's theory of Continental Drift. This was inspired by
the way in which the present continents, if treated as pieces in a
jig-saw, could be fitted together. It postulates that in Permian
times the continents were grouped together and have since
drifted apart. Since the theory has not found general acceptance
little more need be said of it here especially as the figure on
this page is largely self-explanatory.

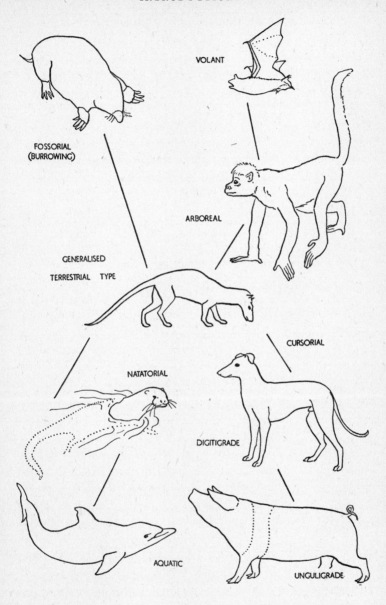

VOLANT

FOSSORIAL
(BURROWING)

ARBOREAL

GENERALISED
TERRESTRIAL TYPE

CURSORIAL

NATATORIAL

DIGITIGRADE

AQUATIC

UNGULIGRADE

6. DIAGRAM EXPRESSING THE LAW OF ADAPTIVE RADIATION

Another aspect of the past is concerned with Osborn's law of Adaptive Radiation. This is more fully expounded in his *Age of Mammals*, where he suggests that each fully isolated region if large and sufficiently varied in its topography, soil, climate and vegetation, will give rise to a diversified mammalian fauna. From primitive central types branches will spring off in all directions with teeth and prehensile organs modified to take advantage of every possible opportunity of securing food, and in adaptation of the body, limbs and feet to habitats of every kind. The larger the region and the more diverse the conditions, the greater the variety of mammals which will result. As shown in the diagram on page 11, Osborn postulated that from a generalised walking and terrestrial type, four lines of evolution can take place. Later writers have modified this to five lines: running or cursorial, swimming or aquatic, burrowing or fossorial, climbing or scansorial, and flying or volant. To an extent, Osborn's law puts into words a concept generally recognised: that in the course of their evolution animals will exploit every possible habitat, and that conversely the range of habitat available will influence their evolution.

If this is truly a law, then it should be capable of application to more groups than mammals since there is no reason to suppose that they differ in principle from the rest of the animal kingdom. Like any other so-called law in biology it will be subject to many exceptions. Throughout the following pages reference will be found to adaptive radiation and the attempt made to apply it more widely than Osborn intended it should be. In fact, it will be used more as a concept against which the relative success of any group can be measured. In a modified form, also, it can be used to measure success even in wholly aquatic groups. Its application to mammals is, however, the more complete, since that group is the latest to appear on the evolutionary scene and our knowledge of it should be the more complete as a consequence. Were our knowledge of extinct birds, reptiles, insects and the rest more complete, there is

the likelihood that it could be applied to them with equal
force.

The incompleteness of the fossil record is proverbial. This
is another point that must be borne in mind in our examinations
which follow. The chances against the remains of any single
animal being preserved as a fossil are great. Moreover, even
in a country like Britain, where the study of fossils has been
extensive over a long period of years, we have little more than
scratched the surface, compared with the remains that still lie
buried. If the maps on pages 8-9 express the geography of past
eras correctly, or nearly so, then the bulk of the fossils should lie
buried in the southern hemisphere. On the other hand, such
fossil evidence as we possess has been derived largely from
the northern hemisphere, from Europe, North America and
parts of Asia. The greater part of Africa remains untouched,
and the same is true for South America, Australia and,
especially, Antarctica; and, if the continent of Gondwanaland was a reality, a great deal must have disappeared under
the sea.

With so many gaps in our knowledge the story of living
fossils is bound to be incomplete; if it were complete it could
not be told within the pages of a single volume. The best that
can be done even now is to bring together the more outstanding
examples and attempt to see the principles underlying their
survival. Although attention is given entirely to living *animal*
fossils, notable examples can also be found in the plant
kingdom. The horsetails (*Equisetum*), for instance, that infest
so many gardens and other cultivated land are the survivors
of a flourishing group of plants which in Carboniferous times
assumed tree-like proportions, the remains of which contributed largely to the formation of coal. More important still
is the maidenhair tree, the Ginkgo, which flourished all over
the world in Mesozoic times, when the giant reptiles roamed the
earth. It was to this that Darwin first gave the name of "living
fossil". The first European to see it was Dr. Engelbrecht
Kaempfer, when he visited Japan in 1690. There it was

growing in the neighbourhood of the sacred shrines, and was apparently unknown in the wild. One specimen at Sendai was 97 feet high and had a girth near the ground of 27 feet. The home of the sacred ginkgos seems, however, to have been China, where they were also planted round the temples.

In more recent times we have had the news of another survivor, the dawn redwood, or *Metasequoia*, also from China. In 1941, Professor T. Kan of the National Central University came across a large tree, 110 feet high, in the Valley of the Tiger, east of Chungking. It was not until 1944, however, that specimens of the cones and foliage were brought back and identified by experts. Then it was realised that this, and the thousand or more other trees like it growing in that sheltered valley, were the survivors of a genus of trees known hitherto only from the Tertiary rocks. Since 1944, seeds and cuttings have found their way over North America and Europe, and the dawn redwood seems likely to follow the ginkgo in the way it was taken from obscurity.

These are but three of a whole range of living plant fossils, and we shall at this point leave the part of the story dealing with them. For different reasons little notice also will be taken of the living fossils among the lower invertebrate animals. Similarly, we shall ignore the Protochordata, the collection of animals including sea-squirts, acorn-worms, lancelets and other even less familiar creatures, even though they play a useful part in indicating the lines along which the early verte-brates came into being. This book may therefore be open to criticism in that it ignores such important groups, but the purpose of such omissions was to keep its narrative in a relatively simple form. In the same way, it will be seen that while much space is devoted to horses and their relatives, as well as camels and tapirs, nothing is said of okapis, giraffes, aardvarks, dassies, and a whole row of others that could be equally well treated as living fossils. Even the humble oyster can boast a long line of ancestors going back to the Cambrian, with little change apart from differences in size. Rather, the aim in this book is to select such examples as best illustrate the principles discussed than to give an exhaustive series of those animals for which there may be a just claim for consideration as living fossils.

CHAPTER I

WHAT IS A LIVING FOSSIL?

WORDS have the habit of changing in meaning from time to time, and the word "fossil" is no exception. Strictly, it means something that is buried, from *fossa*, a pit, derived in turn from the Latin *fodere*, to dig. Fulke, in *Meteors*, published in 1563, writes of "Those bodies that are generated in the earth called *fossilia*", and includes under this heading such things as meteors, metals, chalk and marl. In the first volume of the *Philosophical Transactions of the Royal Society*, dated 1665, we meet the phrase "of Fossile Wood and Coals". At a much later date, Page in his *Handbook of Geological Terms*, dated 1859, uses the word "fossil" for any mineral having a fanciful or supposed resemblance to organic products, as, for example, fossil paper, fossil wood, and the like. It is interesting to note, in passing, that fossil fishes were, in very early times, supposed to be the remains of fishes living in underground waters.

So, from its early use for any rock or mineral dug out of the earth the word is now restricted to "anything found in strata of earth recognisable as the remains of plant or animal or any part thereof", which is the definition given in *Curiosities of Husbandry and Gardening*, dated 1707. Even so, it is difficult to bring this comprehensive definition into general line with what everyone understands by "a fossil". The difficulty of definition can be illustrated by the following example. For several years I observed at intervals the body of a dog lying in the mud at the edge of a slowly meandering stream, which filled up to the limit of its banks in winter and dwindled to little more than a trickle in summer. In time, all that remained was a perfectly cleaned skeleton, lying on its side, with practically every bone in place, slowly disappearing from view in a bed of soft mud. With each winter flood a further layer of silt was added. If nothing has since occurred to disturb it, that skeleton is now lying buried in the mud, in perfect condition, for someone to dig out of the earth in the future. It is a moot point whether that skeleton is deserving of the name, fossil. If it is not, what can we say of the mammoth, the bones of which are dug out of Pleistocene layers, laid down during the last few score millennia? It is always included among the fossil elephants, yet complete carcases, "with flesh, skin and all" have been dug out of the Siberian ice in the last hundred years. Certainly, any mammoth tusks dug up are called fossil ivory.

Perhaps a more telling example is found in the story of the false-killer whale, *Pseudorca crassidens*. This was first known from a skeleton dug out of the Lincolnshire fens and described in 1846, by Sir Richard Owen, who believed it to belong to an extinct species, although he cautiously, and prudently, remarked, "until it should be proved that it still existed in our seas". In 1861 a school of a hundred live false-killers appeared in the Bay of Kiel, and since then many hundreds have been seen, at places as far apart as Scotland, Cape Town and Chatham Island. The original false-killer skeleton is referred to always as a sub-fossil and this term is now used for anything dug out of the earth from strata later than the end of the Pleistocene. In other words, anything buried by natural causes during the last 10,000 years, which is the arbitrary figure used to denote the Holocene (literally, wholly recent), is called a sub-fossil, and anything buried prior to this is truly fossil.

The name "living fossil" arose equally adventitiously, as common names always do, and like most such names is apt and appropriate. They slip easily off the tongue. For these reasons they pass readily into general usage. They are, in fact, catch-phrases, and like all catch-phrases, while expressing a concept which is easily understood and readily recognised, they lack definition, receiving sanction only from habit.

Indeed, for the most part, catch-phrases defy definition. At all events, the name "living fossil" having passed into current scientific jargon, there came a tendency to apply it more and more widely. There were, of course, those things which came obviously within the scope of the name as first used, but it has also come to include those slightly removed from it, even those borderline cases not strictly belonging to the category expressed by the name.

Although, then, it is not possible to define the term precisely, some attempt must be made to examine accepted or possible definitions, if only to convey an approximate idea of the scope of our subject. One accepted definition, as we have seen, is that a living fossil is an organism that has survived beyond its era. No better instance could be given than that of the tuatara of New Zealand. Outwardly the tuatara looks like a lizard, but close examination shows that it is, in fact, the sole survivor of an order of reptiles, the Rhynchocephalia, which flourished in the great Age of Reptiles, and is now extinct except for this one species. Its anatomy shows that tuatara possesses many primitive features and is the most archaic reptile extant. But then there are other living reptiles which possess such primitive features, admittedly not to the degree that tuatara does, and to some of these the term living fossil could conceivably be applied. What marks tuatara as a survivor from former times, in a class of its own, is that it is the sole survivor of its race, occupying a restricted area of the earth's surface, whereas its ancestors were numerous and widespread.

Another favourite example of a living fossil is the king-crab, represented by a few species today, each occupying a very restricted area in the sea. *Limulus,* the name by which the king-crab is usually known, is the sole surviving remnant of an order, the Xiphosura, and of a sub-class, the Delobranchiata, the members of which were most conspicuous in the fresh waters of the Upper Carboniferous period. It has many primitive features and looks totally unlike any other of the Arachnida, the phylum in which it has often been placed, and of which the most familiar members today are the spiders, mites and ticks. In fact, even to a layman's eye it has the appearance of being something out of the past. In addition, its larvae look so very like the extinct Trilobita that no one can have any reasonable doubt that *Limulus* is in truth a living fossil. Although its past history is not so clear-cut as that of the tuatara, we need not hesitate to accept *Limulus* as coming within the scope of our subject, a living fossil whose earliest relatives, now known only from their remains found in the rocks, take us back some 250 million years.

Comparable with *Limulus* are the three species of lungfishes, now confined to the rivers of Australia, Tropical Africa and South America. Fossil lungfishes are first found in the Devonian rocks, suggesting that, in the period known as the Age of Fishes, they were abundant and widespread. In the lungfishes, then, we have something of the pattern seen in the Rhynchocephalia and the Xiphosura: an early period in the Earth's history when the order was abundant and widespread, with now a few survivors, few in number both as to species and individuals, and restricted to one or more widely separated localities. On the other hand, something very similar to this pattern, if not precisely the same, is found in two groups not normally regarded as living fossils. These are the tapirs and the camelids, the camels and llamas. The tapirs are known from two living species, one found in South America and the other in Malaysia, restricted in species and individuals and also restricted to two localised areas, though their ancestors were much more widespread. The same is true for the camelids. The reason why these are not normally spoken of as living fossils is that the history of their respective races cannot be taken back, at the most, more than some 70 million years, and is probably much less. Whatever conclusion we may arrive at, then, regarding a definition of the term, the fact remains that in the minds of most users a long passage of time is a *sine quâ non* of a living fossil.

In a sense, everything living today, plant or animal, is a

3

living fossil, in so far as it represents the surviving generation of an ancient stock, some stocks being more ancient than others. To admit this as a basis of definition would, however, spread the net too widely and, in fact, nullify our use of the term for all practical purposes. Nevertheless, this statement serves to draw attention to the fact that the genealogies of all the main groups of organisms follow a similar pattern, whether they start in the Pre-Cambrian or the Pleistocene. In other words, whether the genealogies are 500 million years old or only 500 thousand. Where one finds such overall similarities of pattern, it is reasonable to assume that the underlying causes are similar and that these should be capable of being reduced to basic principles. This is probably true, although it is doubtful whether our present knowledge is sufficient to permit of this being done adequately.

This pattern, expressed diagrammatically on page 21 shows the main stem and several side-shoots arising from its base. The main stem goes on to proliferate new species, and genera and families, of which some soon die out, others change markedly and by these changes give rise to perceptibly different forms. The side-shoots, the living fossils, are of two kinds at least. The first (the lingerers) are those that persist virtually unchanged and comprise a limited stock. The second differ only in being more numerous in species and populations.

The evolutionary concept of the history of the animal kingdom is usually expressed graphically as a Tree of Descent. Whatever may be the shortcomings of this method, and it can hardly be said to express exactly the true state of affairs, it has the advantage of simplicity and is the best that can be done in a two-dimensional representation. Accepting the Tree as the best means of demonstration, we must visualise the part of it representing the animal kingdom as having a main trunk which divides after a short ascent into two main branches or sub-trunks. The main trunk may be said to represent the mass of early invertebrates of which we have little or no knowledge, those that lived during the fossil-free Pre-Cambrian Period.

7. DIAGRAM REPRESENTING A RECURRENT PATTERN IN EVOLUTION.
To the left, the lingering "living fossil"; centre, the group of archaic
but still successful species, both diverging early from a main stem that
has continued to evolve new forms.

But from it spring several branches which represent the surviving lower invertebrates, each representing a phylum (which is, of course, merely the Latin for a branch) such as the Protozoa, Sponges, Coelenterates, Worms, Echinoderms, Polyzoa and Brachiopods (*see* table, page xiii). The exact relationships between these branches or phyla is not easy to state, and it is of no importance to do so here, except to say that, so far as we can see, certain of the ringed worms (the phylum Annelida) represent an important step forward leading to the formation of the higher Invertebrates and also the Vertebrates, and that the Echinoderms, too, may have affinities with the Vertebrates themselves.

It is, then, somewhere at this point that the two sub-trunks diverge, to represent, on the one hand, the Mollusca and the Arthropoda, which comprise the higher Invertebrates, and the Vertebrates on the other. The picture up to this point is sufficiently vague and obscure for us perhaps to describe the main trunk as shrouded in a ground mist, the mist of time. The position with regard to the two sub-trunks is, however, clearer, and the branches into which they divide can be reason-ably well traced.

Or, again, the various groups of living animals can be set forth in tabular form, as has been done on page xiii. There we find that the Invertebrates comprise nearly a dozen main phyla, with a number of small and somewhat obscure phyla which, for purposes of convenience, are left out of our present consideration. The higher animals, on the other hand, comprise only one phylum with two sub-phyla, the Protochordata and the Vertebrata.

It is quite impossible to describe the classification in simple terms, and even this attempt at simplification leaves the matter still complicated. Some attempt must be made, however, if the study of even a limited number of living fossils is to be put in correct perspective. The whole thing is further complicated by the unfamiliarity of the names of the phyla, and also the uneven values given to them. For example, the birds, which form so familiar, and to the layman's eye, so well-differentiated a group, constitute no more than a class (a sub-division of a phylum), whereas there are phyla of Invertebrates which are made up of a relatively few species of small, unfamiliar and obscure animals. This merely means that they are of peculiar form, sharply marked off from anything else and impossible to pigeon-hole except in a group entirely of their own. The birds, on the other hand, are sometimes described as glorified reptiles, or, in other words, a branchlet, or class. This brief and probably inadequate explanation of the method of classifying the animal kingdom enables us to return to our Tree of Descent and give the further sub-divisions used. As the branches of the tree are successively subdivided into branchlets and twigs of various sizes, so we subdivide the phyla of the animal kingdom into classes, orders, genera and, finally, species, in this descending order.

There is another advantage in using the tree simile in connection with the evolutionary sequence. In studying the geological history of, at least, the main groups, we find that they arise suddenly, wax exceedingly, then go into a slow decline. At the height of their growth they give off a number of branches of unequal length, using length to denote persistence in time. Like the branches and twigs on a tree, some die out early, others continue to live but make little progress, and a few continue in length to outstrip the others. Also, as in the members of a tree, there comes a time when a degeneration sets in and the main branch may begin to die out while the outermost twigs are still healthy; but the dying out, or degeneration, is again uneven, and a rotten branch may have little life left in it, to all intents and purposes it has died away completely, yet one or a few of the outermost twigs may still persist. All such comparisons with the life and death of a tree or any of its members are, of course, only approximate, but it is the nearest familiar object with which it can be compared. Granted this, then the living fossil may be compared with the twigs that still show signs of life after the main branch has died out. The two are also comparable in that the end cannot be long delayed in either.

The use of the Tree of Descent is orthodox. It could, however, equally well be called a Tree of Ascent. It all depends on one's point of view. It is also a matter of personal choice what diagrammatic form one uses to visualise the succession of life through the ages. For my own part, I find irresistible a mental picture comparable to one of those magnificent rockets seen in the more expensive firework displays. The rocket, having reached its zenith, starts to fall and explodes. The cause of the explosion is a spark that has been creeping slowly and unobtrusively along the fuse. At the first explosion a shower of sparks falls, at first gaining in brilliance and later dying out. The life of the individual sparks varies slightly. Some fade out quickly, others die slowly, but from the centre of shower number one comes another explosion, giving shower number two, which closely resembles the first except in colour. In quick succession we see a third, fourth and perhaps a fifth shower, after which such sparks as remain slowly fall to earth, dying out one by one as they go. If at a certain moment we could cause the sparks to hang motionless in the air and could draw a horizontal line just above the lowest line of sparks, we should have a fair representation of the succession of life on the earth, together with its representation today. The horizontal line could be called the beginning of the Holocene. Below it we should see the phyla of animals as they are today, with the most recent groups dominant. Above the line we should see the trails they have left—the fossil record, in fact.

If we could have a rocket so constructed that the first explosion gave rise to a double series of showers, and if each series could consist of a number greater than five, we should have an even better representation of the succession of life. The two series would represent the plant and animal kingdoms respectively, and the slow burning of the fuse which sets the whole thing off could be likened to the slow development of primeval life, of which no fossil trace remains, but which is presumed to have taken place during the early part of the Pre-Cambrian.

And, incidentally, to account for the sudden appearance of whole groups of related but diversified organisms, suddenly as it seems, in the record of the rocks, we have already been driven to use the phrase "explosive evolution". It is, perhaps, signifi- cant that the term, explosive evolution, is used by writers who give no other indication of having had my rocket-simile in mind.

The rocket-simile is, of course, like any other we may use, a rough approximation only, but it has the virtue of simplicity, and, doubtless, of a certain amount of familiarity. It also has the advantage that it will serve well to convey the concept of a living fossil. For example, it sometimes happens that shower number one from a rocket may die out completely by the time the last of its successors has burst before our ecstatic eyes, except for one refractory spark which alone of its contemporaries persists and falls in time and sometimes intermingled with the sparks from later showers. Such a spark represents truly the concept of a living fossil. It is like the fish *Latimeria*, the last of the coelacanths, being emptied on to the deck of a trawler, amid a crowd of herring, cod, whiting, plaice and any other of the species of fishes that have come into being since the rest of the coelacanths died out.

CHAPTER II

NEW ZEALAND RELICS

JOHN EDWARD GRAY published, on page 13 of his Zoological Miscellany, in 1831, a *Note on a peculiar structure in the Head of an Agama.*

> In a skull of an animal allied to *Agama*, or *Uromastyx*, in the College of Surgeons, I have observed that the Ramus of the lower jaw rubs against the lateral processes of the pterygoid bones, so as to prevent the lower jaw from moving from side to side, and that in the species under consideration the hinder part of the upper jaw has a series of teeth about half the length of the outer series placed on a ridge just on the inner edge of the outer teeth, leaving a groove between the two series for the lower jaw to fit into. This skull will doubtless form the type of a new genus, which I purpose to call *Sphaenodon*.

In this unromantic and prosaic manner was introduced to scientific literature one of the most striking of the living fossils. But in 1842, on page 72 of the same journal, Gray published a note on *Descriptions of two hitherto unrecorded species of Reptiles from New Zealand; presented to the British Museum by Dr. Dieffenbach.* One of these he called *Hatteria punctata*, and he also assigned it to the family Agamidae. It so happened that the "lizard" he had named *Hatteria* proved eventually to belong to the same species as the skull he had called *Sphaenodon*. By the laws of zoological nomenclature the first generic name proposed takes priority, and so the species is now known as *Sphenodon punctatus*. Gray was rather given to proposing two different names, even in the same publication, for the same animal and this explains why this particular reptile is sometimes referred to, especially in books of some fifty years ago, as Hatteria and sometimes as Sphenodon.

In his later reference, having described in fair detail the outward appearance of this animal, which he had erroneously supposed to be an Agamid lizard, Gray then gives the notes received from Dr. Dieffenbach. According to these, the animal:

lives in holes, especially on the slopes of the sand hills of the shore. The older missionaries say it was formerly very common, and the natives lived upon it, but for the last fifty years it has been scarcely ever seen. This specimen was found on a small rocky island, two miles from the coast, in the Bay of Plenty, and was given to Dr. Dieffenbach alive, but it shortly died, as it would not eat anything that was offered to it. It is extremely sluggish in captivity, and could be handled without any attempt at resistance or biting. The natives called it *Tuatera*.

Neither Gray nor Dieffenbach had any idea that this scarce but otherwise unpretentious animal would one day prove of sufficient interest to zoologists all over the world to be protected absolutely by law. It was left to Dr. Albert Günther to show, in 1867, that both the original skull and the reptile examined by Gray belonged in fact to one species and that this was one of the most remarkable reptiles alive today, the most spectacular living fossil, the tuatara. Incidentally, the name Tuatera used by Gray and Dieffenbach is, as I understand it, incorrect. According to the dictionary it should be correctly rendered as Tuatara.

The later stages in the history of tuatara are closely linked with the four periods of change in the wild life of New Zealand. The details are taken from Wodzicki's *Introduced mammals of New Zealand*. Prior to the arrival of the Maoris, in the fourteenth century, there is evidence of occupation by man, by the moa-hunters, who are believed to have been partly responsible for the disappearance of the moa and the native swan. The

Maoris, too, had no domestic herbivorous animals, but although they used the indigenous animals for food, there is little to show that they had any marked effect on them. Two species of mammals were introduced, the Polynesian rat and the kuri, or Polynesian dog, but it is believed that neither of these established itself in any numbers. Certainly they were not present in sufficient strength to have any marked effect on the indigenous fauna. The trouble seems to have begun with the second period.

The second and third visits by Captain Cook, in 1774 and 1779, mark the beginning of the second period, when exotic animals were introduced. And between 1779 and the early part of the nineteenth century sealers and whalers had shore bases on New Zealand. They introduced pigs, goats, sheep, cattle, horses, dogs, cats, mice, and the black and the brown rats which must have played havoc with an animal community settled and balanced for so long. The third period, which takes us up to about 1907, saw the rapid influx of the white settler, who not only profoundly changed the nature of the vegetation but increased the introduction of exotic animals. Combined, these had far-reaching effects on the native fauna. From 1907 onwards, however, there was a "growing criticism of the previous policy. A tightening-up of control against indiscriminate liberations and the development of an under-standing of the need for the conservation of national resources began to be evident." If we take Dieffenbach's word, tuatara was already in decline by the middle of the third period, and the changed attitude marking the fourth period, the period of conservation, could only ensure the survival of its remnants.

Today, tuatara is found only on a score or so of islands off the New Zealand mainland, islands covered for the most part with luxuriant vegetation and forming the home of numerous petrels. These are oceanic birds and even in the breeding season, when there are eggs in their nesting burrows, they are not to be seen by day. Either they are far out to sea or, if incubating, are sitting tight on the eggs underground. It is, however, at the

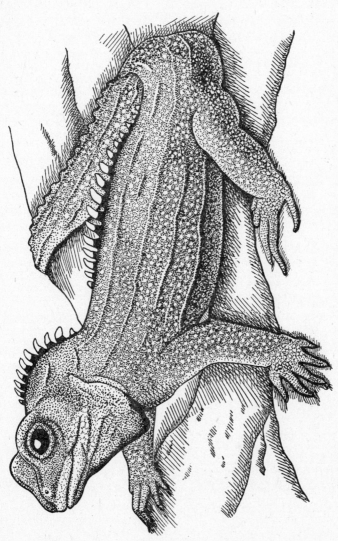

8. TUATARA OF NEW ZEALAND: the lone survivor of a whole group of reptiles.

entrances to these burrows that the tuatara is to be found, for although it can and often does make its own burrow, it shows a preference for one already dug, even if it means sharing it with the petrels. It is the habit of the reptile to lie motionless, by the burrow or on a nearby bank, its greyish colour blending perfectly with the surroundings.

An adult tuatara is some two feet long, of which a third is tail, and running down the middle of the back, from the head to the tail, is a series of spines. It is this feature that is responsible for its name, which is derived from Maori words, *tua* a back and *tara* spiny. The head is large, with prominent ridges over the eyes. The body and tail are laterally compressed, the legs short, and the whole covered with granular scales interspersed with larger tubercles. In fact, tuatara has the general appearance of a large lizard or a small crocodile. The crest of spines, most prominent on the head and back, and forming a saw-edge along the mid-line of the tail, are less fearsome than they look, being soft and flexible. Possibly they are the vestige of a defensive armament possessed by its ancestors, for prior to the settlement of New Zealand by the Maoris the tuatara probably had few if any enemies, and such defensive measures as it might have been compelled to take lay in its immobility, its harmony with the background and, if more active defence were needed, its speed and its teeth. Although habitually lethargic, the animal can move with speed if the need arises; and its powerful jaws can be snapped to with precision, giving a bite to be avoided. Moreover, once it has closed its jaws it does not readily let go.

Lethargy is, however, the outstanding feature of this reptile. Even the developing embryo seems to show the family trait, for although it grows rapidly for the first four months, it then ceases for the winter, from March to September—a kind of hibernation within the egg.

The female tuatara lays 10 to 13 leathery-shelled eggs, which she buries a few inches beneath the surface in a shallow trench covered with earth and leaves, leaving them to be hatched by the heat of the sun. The young are hatched thirteen months later, fully able to fend for themselves. They are then about six inches long and are at first capable of showing considerable activity. They grow rapidly at this time, but in succeeding years the growth rate slows down markedly. This much is suggested from specimens kept in captivity, but whether there is the same display of juvenile activity in the wild is open to doubt. For example, there is a record of one young tuatara in captivity that ran and jumped about for four days without resting. Then it died, and the assumption is that it had used up "the amount of energy that is efficient normally for the whole life span". In point of fact, loss of sleep or rest, in any animal, including human beings, can be lethal, and there is a short limit in any species to which sustained activity can be continued without fatal results. On the other hand, it is not impossible that it died of heatstroke. Even so, this observation merely serves to underline what has been called the outstanding characteristic of the reptile in question, its habitual and extreme lethargy. It may even be the secret of its long survival when all related species have died out.

Conservation of energy by an habitual lethargy seems usually to be linked with a long life-span. The tortoise not only beats the hare in the race, as told in the fable, but in its tenacity for living. The linkage for longevity and lethargy applies, however, more to the species than to the individual. So far as the tuatara is concerned there is only fragmentary evidence for this. We know that specimens have been kept in Dunedin for over fifty years; and the Maoris tell of one that lived in a shell pit on Motiti Island for nearly three hundred years. This record, like any given for tortoises may, of course, be exaggerated. We have no proof one way or the other. There are, similarly, several records of long life in tortoises, but there is only one undisputed record, that for Marion's tortoise, which is known beyond a doubt to have lived for over 150 years. Even so there are others, fairly dependable, that take the life-span of a tortoise to 250 years. It is of interest to note, also, that there is a rough connection to be found between the longevity and the period of gestation, or, alternatively, the rate of incubation. It seems to be a fairly reliable guide when comparing related species, but less dependable when comparing species belonging to different orders. The rate of incubation for the tuatara is thirteen months, which is remarkably long for an animal of that size, being nearly double that for the larger tortoises, which can be put at about eight months. For the smaller tortoises, it is only three to four months. Even on this rough basis, and even if the longevity of tortoises be put, conservatively, at 150 years, a longevity of 300 years for tuatara need not be out of question.

Supporting evidence for an extraordinary longevity in the tuatara can be adduced from what is known of its rate of living, the metabolic rate, as it is called. This, in any case, is much lower than that of a tortoise, for while the tuatara has been credited with a fair turn of speed on occasion, tortoises can, despite habitual appearances to the contrary, be positively vivacious by comparison. The precise scientific evidence for this is striking. Dr. R. D. Milligan, in his investigations on the respiration and metabolism of the tuatara, found that the output of carbon dioxide at a temperature of 6–8° C. was 2·3 c.c. per hour for every kilogram of body weight. This can be compared with the 12·8 c.c. output of carbon dioxide by a hibernating lizard. Dr. Milligan also watched a tuatara for one hour without seeing any signs of respiration. This, of course, merely serves to stress the incredibly slow rate of the life processes of tuatara. Even under normal summer conditions, the animal respires once only in every seven seconds, and this probably represents the maximum rate. Another small observation illustrating this lethargy is that a tuatara will often go to sleep with a piece of food held tightly in its mouth, falling asleep in the act of chewing.

Tuatara normally feeds at night, hunting beetles, flies and centipedes. It probably takes other things besides, for in captivity it has been found to eat snails, and has even been induced to take raw meat, although usually, like snakes and lizards, it will take nothing that is not moving. As to quantity of food, it was found, in captivity and at the height of its summer activity, that two snails a day were sufficient to satisfy it. The method of hunting is to crawl up to its prey, raise the front part of the body, arch the neck, then suddenly pounce. And after this display of activity, the customary lethargy supervenes: tuatara masticates slowly, with a long interval between each bite.

In spite of all that has been said, those who have had the good fortune to observe this animal closely in captivity regard it as moderately intelligent, relatively to the general run of reptiles. Intelligence, or perhaps in this case we should say mental capacity, is never easy to assess, and no experimental work and comparatively little observation of this particular beast has been possible. The statement rests therefore on such facts as their inquisitiveness, their alertness to unusual sounds and their tameability. Tame tuataras will recognise and show confidence in persons with whom they are familiar and will show timidity towards strangers, or even a vicious display of temperament. How far these things can be attributed to intelli-gence is a matter of individual opinion. They do suggest, on the other hand, an acute awareness of what is going on around and the possession of sense-organs that work more quickly than the general habits of the animal might suggest.

The persistence of tuatara over so long a time, its survival beyond the rest of its race, may perhaps be attributed to several causes. First, it appears to have had a comparative freedom from enemies until, at least, the second period of the human settlement of New Zealand. The fossil record of the Rhyncho-cephalia dates from Triassic times and fairly soon after what is now New Zealand became severed from any continental land-mass. One consequence of this was that the territory which subsequently gave rise to New Zealand in its modern form received no immigration of mammals. The true flightless birds reached it, including the giant moas. How far these preyed upon tuatara or its ancestors can only be surmised. The probability is that they did not do so, but, in any case, natural predators do not, save under exceptional circumstances, bring about the extinction of their prey (*see* Chapter 14).

Coupled with this freedom from enemies is the conservation of energy and a slow rate of living, these things being linked with a long period of incubation and, so far as can be seen, an unusual longevity. There is, however, another factor which may have contributed largely to tuatara's survival, especially during the later period of the history of the Rhynchocephalia as a whole. It could even be, but this is pure conjecture, that its association with the petrels and penguins is the reason why this one species of Rhynchocephalia held on when the others became extinct. The early history of birds, as a class, is almost unknown, but we know that petrels date from the early Tertiary, though we have no means of telling how quickly the tuatara learned to live with them. We only know what happens today: that the birds make burrows and occupy them during the breeding season; that tuatara may occupy with the birds the same chamber at the end of the burrow, apparently leaving the chicks and eggs unmolested. Sometimes the burrow is forked, in which case the tuatara usually occupies the right-hand fork. In any case, in winter the reptile has the burrow to itself, when it digs in at the end of it to hibernate. The hibernation is not complete in that the tuatara is capable of movement if disturbed. Rather is it a period of even greater lethargy. The main point is that for some time past the tuatara has had its home prepared for it, and this may have helped in the later stages of its survival.

Where no prefabricated burrow is available the tuatara will scrape one for itself, both for its ordinary daily purposes and for the winter resting period. In such case, it is a shallow affair. To pursue the suggestion made above, it may be that the good fortune of being able to use burrows made by the birds not only saves energy but also gives greater protection against the elements even if no living enemies have to be avoided. It may even be that such burrows also ensure an easy food supply, since the suggestion has been put forward that the birds profit by this partnership, in that the tuatara devours the parasites and other insects that tend to accumulate around the nest. It is, however, doubtful if the reptile eats such small insects. There is also the suggestion that as the birds die off, the reptiles are left wholly in possession of the burrows, since old tuataras are found living in moss-grown burrows. Generally speaking, therefore, we get the impression that tuatara has in several ways had living made easy.

It should be explained here that the Rhynchocephalia as a whole were not confined to New Zealand, their fossil remains having been found in Europe, America, Asia and Africa. It has been suggested that the tuatara was able to survive in New Zealand, with its temperate climate, because of its low body temperature, $52°$ F. when the animal is active. In all other living reptiles it is never less than $65°$ F. when the animal is active. This is, however, pure speculation, since we can have no evidence that other members of the Rhynchocephalia had a higher body temperature. The fact that the tuatara suffered grievously from the introduction of cats, dogs and rats suggests rather that its isolation on islands free from mammalian predators was more important in its continued survival.

So far it has been taken for granted that tuatara really is an archaic survivor, and it is now time to give the reasons upon which this assumption is made. Although lizard-like, tuatara is no lizard but a representative of an order, the Rhynchocephalia, which can be traced back in an almost unbroken series to the Triassic, 180 million years ago. Zoologically, the order Rhynchocephalia is of equal rank with the three other orders of existing reptiles, the Testudines (tortoises and turtles), the Loricata (crocodiles) and the Squamata (lizards and snakes). On the other hand, it is not closely related to any of these, differing especially in its internal structure. The bones of the skull are shaped and disposed in the manner of those in the skull of crocodiles, another very ancient group of reptiles, the ancestry of which can be traced back also to the Triassic.

Another peculiarity is that the teeth, instead of being detachable, as in most vertebrates, are actually fused to the jawbone.

4

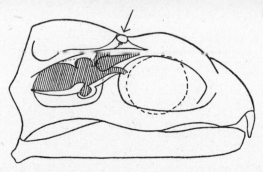

9. SKULL AND BRAIN OF TUATARA; an arrow indi-
cates the pineal or third eye, a mere pinhead underlying
the pineal plug which fills the hole in the top of the
skull. The size of the paired eye is shown by the
dotted circle.

The most interesting feature of the skull is, however, the
opening in the roof, because it is beneath this that is found the
so-called pineal eye, also known as the parietal eye, from its
position in that bone of the skull. The first name originates
from the appendage in the human brain known as the pineal
body or pineal gland, in reference to a supposed resemblance
to a pine-cone. The human pineal body is small and conical,
and reddish-grey. It arises as a hollow outgrowth from the roof
of the third ventricle of the brain. Its function is unknown, and
because it is unpaired it was at one time thought by some
philosophers to be the seat of the soul. In most existing vertebrates it is in this same form, and its origin would have been
as puzzling as its function but for what has been found and
investigated in certain reptiles, including tuatara. In larval
lampreys and in some lizards, the pineal body is stalked,
bringing it closer under the roof of the skull, and in them it has
the structure of an eye, with a more or less distinct retina and
lens, and is called the pineal or median eye. And although there
is a tendency to overstate the importance of its discovery in
tuatara, it does form an essential clue to such understanding as
we have of this organ.

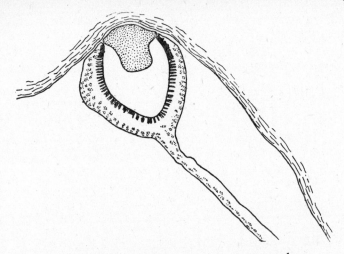

10. PINEAL EYE OF TUATARA ENLARGED, to show the optic nerve, retina and lens.

This foramen in the roof of the skull is so widespread a feature of fossil amphibia and reptiles as to leave little doubt that to the ancestors of all modern amphibia and reptiles the pineal eye was an important sense-organ. In the course of evolution it has degenerated and the vestige has taken on the form of a ductless gland; it is in this form that we find it especially in living birds and mammals. The importance of its discovery in tuatara lies in this, that it has the characters of a simple eye. Although it is covered by skin and is invisible from the outside, except in the young animal, it has the appearance of an eye that has only lately ceased to function as such. Furthermore, there is evidence of its being the remains of a pair. This most completely developed eye is the left eye of the pair. The right eye is represented in tuatara by an elongated body, having now little obvious likeness to an eye, lying beneath the left one, and leaving little doubt, from its mode of development, that it is the right eye of a pair.

Tuatara has brought down to the present time, then, in living form, many features peculiar to the Dinosaurs, Ichthyosaurs,

Plesiosaurs and other extinct reptiles. In the structure of the skull there is a link between the early crocodiles and the ancestral birds. In addition, it has abdominal ribs like those of Ichthyosaurs and Plesiosaurs, and serving the same function as the abdominal plates of tortoises and turtles, thus exposing the closeness of the ancestors of both the Rhynchocephalia and the Testudines, even though their modern descendants have diverged in so many other features. The ribs, too, bear back/ wardly projecting processes similar to those found in crocodiles and birds.

It may be as well to make an interruption here, to explain that when we speak of an animal as archaic or primitive, it does not mean that everything about it is primitive. Nor, when we speak of an animal as advanced or specialised does it mean that it has no primitive features. Thus, tuatara is referred to as the most archaic or primitive living reptile. Tortoises and croco/ diles are also spoken of as archaic. Lizards, by contrast, are more advanced. Yet, although tuatara still possesses the remains of a pineal eye, and in crocodiles it has degenerated still further, in some lizards it is more complete than in tuatara. Similarly, tuatara and lizards have the ability to throw off the tail, by means of a special breaking plane, and to regenerate the lost part, but neither tortoises nor crocodiles can do this. On the other hand, the young tuatara escapes from the egg on hatching by cutting through the shell with a hardened knob of skin on the snout, known as a caruncle. Young tortoises and crocodiles also have a caruncle, while young lizards have an egg/tooth, which is like a true tooth, with enamel, dentine and a pulp cavity. Incidentally, the young platypus, which we shall examine in the next chapter, a mammal that preserves several reptilian features, has both a caruncle and an egg/tooth.

Without going into more detail, therefore, we may count tuatara as both a "missing link" and a "living fossil", and it is good to know that the Animals Protection Act of New Zealand gives absolute protection to this "voice from the past". However, tuatara is only one among several interesting

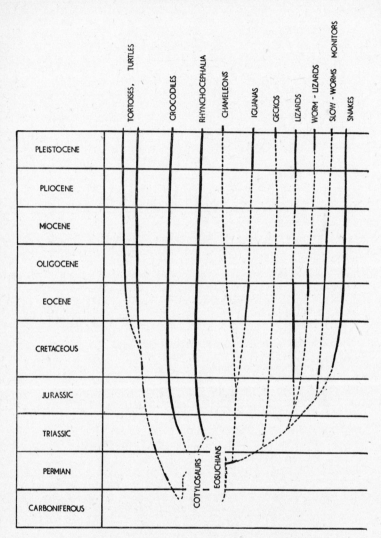

II. EVOLUTION OF THE REPTILES: to show the groups living today and their fossil lineages.

survivors in this part of the world. Another is the Stephens Island frog. So, we turn to a small island, only 500 acres in extent, lying between the North and South Islands of New Zealand, where live the surviving remnants, so it is believed by some zoologists, of the original family from which all living frogs have descended. Known as the Stephens Island frog after the island it inhabits, it is $1\frac{1}{2}$ in. long, and a golden-brown, with irregular black markings on the legs and body. The head is marked with a black line running from the snout to behind the eyes and with a light brown triangle on top of the head. The eyes are large and black. Outwardly, the main difference between it and the more typical frogs lies in the absence of webbing to the toes, and the unusually large eyes. Internally, the ribs and the pattern of the veins recall those of newts and fishes. Little is known about the early stages in its life history, and the frog itself is too rare and so seldom seen that it may be some time before anything is discovered. But it seems probable that in the Stephens Island frog the tadpole stage is passed within the egg.

On the present home of the Stephens Island frog the shores rise steeply in rugged cliffs and tussock-covered slopes to about a thousand feet. It is under the boulders at the top of the island that these amphibians are found, and although the island had received considerable attention from biologists since the 1890's, when tuatara was found there in some numbers, the frog was not found until 1917. At that time the boulder bank forming its home was re-covered with trees; but now nothing is left of them except a few dying specimens. This bank, 60 by 80 feet, with the boulders a few feet deep, is now exposed to wind and sun, and although it is probably fairly humid beneath the boulders there is no water, still or running.

The frog is so rare that in spite of constant searches very few have been found. After the first was found, in 1917, the late Dr. J. Thompson, then Director of the New Zealand Dominion Museum, "enlisted the aid of the lighthouse-keepers' families in an endeavour to collect more specimens, but this combined team searched the bank fruitlessly for a week, and were about to abandon the search when a number of frogs were found together under one large boulder". Another team, several years later, searched for several days before finding any, and a subsequent expedition of American naturalists found only two. During the Second World War, when hundreds of men visited the island to garrison it at different times, a number of searches were made, but only two frogs were found. These were photographed and released. That was in 1942, and from then until 1950, no more were found, in spite of a number of visits made by groups of naturalists especially for the purpose of looking for them. It began to look as if the animal was indeed extinct. Then, in 1950, Mr. W. H. Dawbin found one after three days of searching; and three months later another five were found, all of which were photographed, measured and released.

The small numbers found, and the need for conserving them, means that we know practically nothing of the frog's habits or life-history. The few that were taken away for further study did not survive. The most it is possible to say of it is, therefore, that it seems to need a special kind of habitat, and that its adaptability to changed circumstances and its tenacity of life are alike low. If, indeed, the Stephens Island frog is a representative of "the original family from which all frogs have sprung", then it has survived comparatively unchanged for at least 35 million years, and possibly more than double this time.

We can but speculate on this and ask a number of questions. Why, first of all, should it be assumed that this frog is so primitive that it carries us back to the early ancestors of all frogs? First, there is the fact that it has ribs. This may be assumed to be a primitive character, since, if the Amphibia as a whole sprang from a fish-like ancestor, then it is reasonable to assume that the earliest Amphibia had ribs. Yet the majority of present-day frogs do not have them and may be presumed to have lost them secondarily. The earliest representatives of Amphibia, those of the Upper Devonian and the Carboniferous,

12. STEPHENS ISLAND FROG, probably the most
archaic frog alive today.

certainly had ribs, lizard-like ribs, and these, or the remains
of them are found today in the Stephens Island frog. A few
other frogs in New Zealand also have them, which is significant. And apart from these few species, the only other frogs
in the world today to have them are the ribbed frogs of
the North-West U.S.A. The presence of ribs can, therefore,
be regarded as a primitive character.

Perhaps the most significant character of the species under
discussion is, however, the feet. These are without webs, and if
our interpretation of the fossil evidence is correct, frogs have
descended from tailed ancestors much like our present-day
newts and salamanders in form if not in size. These had the
four legs more or less equal in length and the toes free. The
much lengthened hind-legs and toes, the webbing of the toes
and the return to a more aquatic habitat, seen in most modern
frogs, are all secondary characters. Furthermore, the extended
period of aquatic life of the tadpole, found in so many modern
frogs, must also be secondary, although it has come to resemble

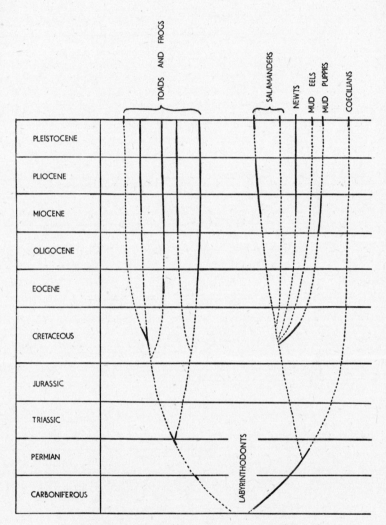

13. EVOLUTION OF THE AMPHIBIA: to show the relationship of frogs to the other amphibia.

the similarly aquatic stage of the tailed amphibia from which frogs have been derived.

Australia and New Zealand are the home of so many primitive forms that it is natural to look there for survivors in all groups of animals. In New Zealand, in addition to the Stephens Island frog, there are other frogs, less localised in their distribution, which also have primitive characters. One of these was first made known in 1861. It had, in fact, been discovered a few years earlier, but was unknown to the Maoris. Known by its generic name only—that is, it has no common name—*Liopelma* has small ribs like those of the North American ribbed frogs, vertebrae like those of fossil amphibia and unlike those of any living today, and veins resembling those of newts and fishes. Moreover, *Liopelma* lives under stones, logs and boulders, on the crests of hills, under conditions, in fact, very like those in which the Stephens Island frog is found. Although it has been found sitting in water, this type of frog does not pass through a tadpole stage in the usual sense. The tadpole develops within a capsule inside the egg, moving about in the fluid within the capsule. Before leaving the egg, it grows its legs, begins to resorb its tail and hatches as a small frog similar to the adult except for a short tail.

The fossil record of frogs goes back to the Jurassic, although it is suspected that it may yet be found to date from the Carboniferous. In view of the earlier separation of New Zealand from neighbouring land-masses, therefore, it is reasonable to expect the isolation of archaic frogs on its islands, an expectation which is supported by the findings of comparative anatomy.

CHAPTER III

THE EGG-LAYING MAMMALS

D<small>R. GEORGE SHAW</small> was born at Bierton, in the county
of Buckinghamshire, in 1751. The son of a vicar, he
went into the Church in due course, but an early love
of natural history still persisted. He left the Church and took a
medical degree. Later he was appointed lecturer in botany at
Oxford, but after a few years came to London to practise
medicine. In 1788 he took part in the foundation of the Linnean
Society of London, of which he was one of the first vice-
presidents, and before long was elected a Fellow of the Royal
Society. In 1794 he became an assistant-keeper in the natural
history section of the British Museum. Clearly a man of parts
and of ability, Dr. Shaw had yet to experience what, for us
looking back, appears as a red letter day in an eventful life.
This was when he first handled and examined a platypus. The
event probably did not assume such an importance for him as
might appear to us now, and whether he felt any thrill at this
experience history does not record.

The first recorded time that the platypus was seen in Australia
by a European was in the year 1797, nearly two hundred years
after the earliest discovery of the kangaroo, which must have
puzzled the crew of the Dutch vessel, the *Batavia*, who first saw
it on Abrolhos Island. But, if we may judge by the names given
it, the platypus seems to have been even more puzzling. The
first Europeans to see it in the wild noted that it had "instead
of the mouth of an animal, the upper and lower mandibles of
a duck", and it was variously named the duckbill, watermole
and duckmole, all expressive of its outstanding characteristics.
A skin was sent to England, in 1799, and Dr. Shaw and other

45

scientists who examined this had severe doubts as to its authenticity. At that time, the Chinese had already earned a reputation for manufacturing fictitious animals, such as mer-maids, to sell to Europeans, and the ship carrying the skin had come by way of the "Indian Seas", which made this particular piece of cargo suspect.

The many works published by Dr. Shaw include his *Naturalists' Miscellany*, and in volume 10, dated 1799, we can read what he had to say of this strange beast from "down under":

> Of all the Mammalia yet known it seems the most extraordinary in its conformation; exhibiting the perfect resemblance of the beak of a Duck engrafted on the head of a quadruped. So accurate is the similitude that, at first view, it naturally excites the idea of some deceptive preparation by artificial means: the very epidermis, proportion, serratures, manner of opening and other particulars of the beak of a shoveler, or other broad-billed species of duck, presenting themselves to the view: nor is it without the most minute and rigid examination that we can persuade ourselves of its being the real beak or snout of a quadruped.

Clearly Shaw was impressed by its appearance but very cautious, even suspicious, and whether it was he or not, some-body tried to prise the duck bill from the skin with a pair of scissors. The skin was in the possession of a Mr. Dobson, in 1799, "distinguished by his exquisite manner of preparing specimens of vegetable anatomy". Now it is in the collections of the British Museum (Natural History), and the marks of the scissors can still be seen.

Shaw concludes his description of the platypus with these words:

> On a subject so extraordinary as the present, a degree of scepticism is not only pardonable, but laudable; and I ought perhaps to acknowledge that I almost doubt the testimony of my own eyes with respect to the structure of the animal's

14. THE DUCKBILL OR PLATYPUS of Australia, one
of the most archaic mammals alive today.

beak; yet must confess that I can perceive no appearance of
any deceptive preparation; and the edges of the rictus, the
insertion, etc., when tried by the test of maceration in water,
so as to render every part completely moveable seem perfectly
natural; nor can the most accurate examination of expert
anatomists discover any deception in this particular.

By 1844 much more was known of the duckbill, when Dr.
William B. Carpenter, lecturer on Natural History and Comparative Anatomy at St. Thomas's Hospital, London, published his *Popular Cyclopaedia of Natural Science*. In volume
I, page 354, he refers again to the scepticism of the earlier
naturalists, and to their suspicion of "the bill of a Bird having
been artificially attached to the skin of an Otter-like Quadruped.
This, however, was soon found not to be the case; the combination being one effected by the hand of Nature, and serving
(with others of a similar character) to draw together the classes
of Mammals, Birds, and Reptiles, which previously appeared
to be so widely separated." Already, therefore, the platypus
was recognised as a link joining the three classes, a missing

link as we now popularly call such animals; in fact, a living
fossil, although Gray does not use the term. Again we have a
detailed description of the animal, followed by an account of
its reproduction. And in this last we realise that the egg-laying
character of the platypus was then unknown and formed no
part of the deductions of contemporary zoologists regarding its
link with the past.

According to Carpenter:

> The young are produced in a very imperfect state, and are
> very unlike the fully-developed animal. The skin is entirely
> destitute of fur, and is thrown, by the curling of the body,
> and the doubling of the head and tail beneath it, into
> transverse folds; the eyes are not formed, and their place is
> merely indicated by the presence of a few wrinkles of the
> skin. The margin of the bill is at that time soft, and the tongue
> (which in the adult does not extend between the mandibles)
> advances to its front edge; so that the young animal can
> obtain nourishment by sucking, which was at first thought
> impossible. The mammary gland of the female is very simple
> in structure, and is divided into a large number of separate
> lobes; this is just what might be expected, when it is
> remembered that the organ here makes its first appearance,
> and presents, therefore, its lowest grade of formation. The
> Ornithorhyncus is *truly* ovo-viviparous; for the embryo
> appears never to derive any other sustenance from its parent,
> up to the time of its birth, than that which is stored up for it
> in the ovum; but, as in some Lizards and Fishes, the egg is
> hatched (as it were) within the oviduct, so that the young
> is born alive.

In this way, platypus made its entry upon the scientific stage,
and there is no hint in its first lines of the information it was
later to yield. The peculiarity of the duckbill may have aston-
ished the early zoologists, giving rise to much speculation and
comment. It also provides the rather amusing story of their
cautious approach to it, of the suspicion that a hoax was being
played on them, and the attempt to unmask the hoax with the

aid of a pair of scissors. The real interest in platypus was yet to come, however, and could only be revealed by the patience of the comparative anatomists, for apart from the possession of the duckbill, there is little unusual in the animal. When fully grown it is some 2 feet long, of which 6 inches is tail. The body is rounded and barrel-shaped, the tail is broad and flattened, the legs short and bearing strong claws. It has no external ear, and the eyes are small and obscured by the fur. One of its earlier common names, the duckmole, is therefore readily understandable. Its fur is thick and soft, with long crisp and curly hairs and a dark underfur, the whole body appearing sepia brown above and silvery tinged with yellow or pink underneath. The male has, on the inside of each hind-leg, a hollow horny spur connected with a poison gland, probably used for defence.

Essentially aquatic, the habitat of the platypus is the high mountain streams extending well down into the warm lowland waters, where it spends most of its time in water, using the banks for shelter. The fore-feet are adapted for this dual purpose. They are webbed, with the webbing extending well beyond the toes to assist the animal in swimming but capable of being folded back to leave the claws free for burrowing and for walking on land. The hind-feet are also webbed but not so extensively as the fore-feet. The bill, or, we should say, the beak-like muzzle, purple-black above and a mottled yellow and black below, is highly sensitive, for seeking out the worms, crayfish and other small invertebrates living in the mud. In common with so many mammals, platypus has cheek pouches for the temporary storage of food. The jaws are armed inside with horny plates, for the mastication of food, but in the young animal there are two or three pairs of teeth in the upper jaw and two pairs in the lower jaw. Platypus is energetic and restless and, like all small mammals of this disposition, it consumes its own weight of food each day.

The banks of the streams are used for constructing the nesting burrows, elaborate systems of tunnels which, although never more than a foot below the surface, may be between 24 and 60 feet long. The nesting chamber is at the end of a tortuous tunnel which is blocked at intervals by walls of soft earth, up to 8 inches thick, tamped into position by the female's tail. The nest itself is of grass and leaves forming a rounded mass, the materials being collected and transported with the tail. In it the female lays, usually two, soft-shelled, dirty-white eggs, three-quarters of an inch in diameter, and then does not leave the nest until they are hatched. The young remain blind for eleven weeks after hatching, and stay in the nest for a month after this, taking to the water when they are four months old.

Today we accept without a second thought that platypus is an egg-laying mammal, a link with the reptiles and a living representative of the early mammals that diverged from the main reptilian stock. These opinions have been arrived at only after considerable research and the fitting together of a mass of detailed evidence. They were not originally apparent in this form and one of them was not accepted for a long time. Platypus was first seen in 1797, as we have said, but the fact that it laid eggs, despite an account of the actual egg-laying published in Australia, was not accepted until, after much controversy and not until eighty years later, Caldwell made a special journey to Australia to study the animal's habits on the spot. The zoologist is probably no more incredulous and unwilling to accept evidence for things outside his ordinary experience than other people. Even so, serious mistakes are often made, and it has happened again and again that false stories have been accepted by the zoological world and are still perpetuated. It has also happened that others, ultimately proved to be true, have had to be forced under the zoological nose before being accepted. This does mean, however, that in the main any assertions made by these scientists are likely to be founded on the firmest evidence.

A mammal that lays eggs suggests immediately an affinity with birds and reptiles, but the claim to this relationship for platypus is based less on the egg-laying than on the internal anatomy which shows a mixture of reptilian and mammalian characters. It will, however, be more profitable to postpone consideration of these until after the discussion of a closely related Australian mammal, the echidna or spiny anteater, so that we may compare and contrast the two animals.

Platypus was first classified with the anteaters and other animals that were later to be grouped together as the Edentata, or toothless ones; but already in 1798, Cuvier, the celebrated French naturalist, in his *Tableau élémentaire de l'Histoire naturelle des Animaux*, had added another, the echidna, the name of which is derived from the Greek for a viper, an echidna in Greek mythology being a monster half maiden and half serpent. This gives some indication of what the naturalists of the time thought of this strange beast, the size of a hedgehog, with a long snout and a long sticky, extensile tongue for picking up ants. Cuvier, in the work quoted, dismisses the "monster" in a few prosaic words: "spiny anteaters with the body covered with quills. Only one species is known, from New Holland, with the legs and tail excessively short."

Carpenter, for his part, tells us that:

The echidna, or Porcupine Anteater, seems at first sight very different in its conformation from the Ornithorhincus; but in the most important particulars of its structure it closely resembles it, though differing widely in its habits, and in all the peculiarities connected with them. It is about the size and form of a Hedgehog, which it also resembles in having its body covered with spines; but these are much stouter than in that animal.

He also adds details of its behaviour:

It inhabits the mountain ranges of Australia, and is found also in Van Diemen's Land and the islands of Bass's Straits. It burrows with great rapidity; and will even work its way under a pretty strong pavement, or the foundation of a wall, removing the stones with its claws. When attacked by dogs,

5

it quickly sinks into the earth or sand, so as to present nothing but its prickly back to its adversaries. In one instance, a large chest of earth containing plants being given to an echidna in captivity, it made its way to the bottom in less than two minutes. This individual is described as stupid and inert; and for the first month after its capture, it took no food whatever. It became very thin, but did not appear to suffer. It afterwards ate a mixture of flour, water, and sugar, upon which it lived for some time. It made frequent efforts to get out of its cage, and displayed very great strength. The possessor of another captive echidna speaks of it as in his opinion the strongest Quadruped for its size, in existence. To lift it from the ground requires more force than would be supposed; so firmly does it fix itself to the earth, by means of its powerful feet and claws.

As with platypus, our knowledge of echidna has been considerably advanced since the first accounts of it, but mainly in regard to its anatomy. A summary of its appearance and habits is as follows. Looking rather like a large hedgehog, with the body a little more flattened, it has no tail or external ears. The upper parts of the body are clothed with a mixture of spines and hair, and the underparts are hairy. The muzzle, long and beak-like, is very sensitive, for seeking out the ants on which it feeds; the tongue is long and extensible for picking up these as well as termites and other small insects. The jaws are without teeth and the insects are ground between the palate and a series of horny serrations on the back of the tongue. The toes are armed with stout claws, such effective digging organs that in soft soil the echidna can sink beneath the surface in next to no time. In captivity, echidna will eat almost anything small enough to be sucked up through the tiny mouth, such as minced meat, or bread and milk. Moreover, it is able to fast without detriment, as Carpenter reports, for as much as a month at a time, which is in sharp contrast to platypus and more in line with what is found in amphibia and reptiles. In cold weather it will hibernate.

15. ECHIDNA OR SPINY ANTEATER of Australia,
like platypus, lays eggs, and is also a survivor from
the past.

Like the hedgehog, echidna is an inconspicuous animal,
burrowing into the earth or under logs or stones. It shares with
other burrowing animals an unusual strength, being able to
move stones and logs in its search for food.

The female echidna deposits her single egg in an abdominal
pouch and, after hatching, the young is carried about in the
pouch for some weeks. After this, she leaves it in a safe place
to rest and grow before setting out on its own.

There are several species of echidna, the Australian and a
number of others living in New Guinea. These latter are larger,
with longer snouts and the spines are less numerous and almost
completely concealed by a black fur. The one species of
platypus and the several species of echidna comprise the sub-
class Prototheria or Monotremata, and in all species the internal
anatomy is a mixture of reptilian and mammalian characters.

There would be little gained by a detailed recital of the
minutiae of the anatomy, which can be obtained from any
text-book, and a summary of them will suffice to indicate their
significance. In the Monotremes, the skull is reptilian, notably

in the pterygoid bones, the presence of a prevomer, and an epipterygoid; and a narrow canal in the temporal region seems to be the homologue of the posterior temporal fossa of the ichthyosaurs and plesiosaurs. On the other hand, each half of the lower jaw is mammalian, consisting of a single bone, whereas in reptiles, as in amphibia and fishes, it is composed of a number of separate bones; and although none of the mono-tremes has teeth in the adult stage, those present in the young platypus are unlike the teeth of any other mammals. The ear-bones are on the way to the typical mammalian condition, except that there is no bony auditory bulla as in modern mammals. The neck vertebrae bear separate ribs, as in the dinosaurs and other extinct reptiles, while the dorsal ribs are much more numerous than in other mammals and approach more nearly the condition found in reptiles. Moreover, the ribs do not articulate with the transverse processes but directly with the bodies of the vertebrae. The limb girdles and the bones of the limbs themselves are shaped very like those of reptiles. On the whole, therefore, the skeletons of monotremes may be said to be largely reptilian, with several features in common, more especially, with some of the extinct reptiles, but with a few characteristics, particularly in the skull, similar to or approach-ing the condition found in mammals.

The soft parts of the body show the same mixed or inter-mediate characters. The rectum and the urinogenital systems open into a common cloaca, a feature of all reptiles and amphibia. The only other mammals to show this are the mar-supials. The brain is large compared with that of reptiles and is constructed very much on the mammalian plan, the pallial areas of the cerebral hemispheres being well developed, and although the cerebral hemispheres themselves are smooth on the surface in platypus, they are convoluted in echidna. The corpus callosum of the typical mammal is, however, absent, the heart resembles that of mammals, and there is a single aortic arch, on the left, as in other mammals, whereas in birds it is on the right and in reptiles it is paired. The thorax and abdomen are separated by a diaphragm, as in mammals. On the other hand, although the heart and main blood-vessels are mammalian, and the monotreme is warm-blooded, the mechanism for the regula-tion of the body temperature is imperfect as compared with typical mammals, and the temperature itself is lower and more variable.

Not only is it possible to see in such details of structure a transition from the reptilian to the mammalian conditions, but by close study of the characteristics of fossil reptiles and mammals, and the comparison of these with the living species, there emerges the strong probability that the monotremes represent a stock which diverged from the main mammalian stock in the Jurassic period some 150 million years ago. On the other hand, no remains of monotremes have been found earlier than the Pleistocene, less than one million years ago. Thus we have the anomaly of a living fossil with few fossil antecedents known; and these, at best, are little more than sub-fossil.

Assuming that the monotremes may be justly regarded as living fossils, the interest then lies in speculating on the circumstances that have made their survival possible. In both platypus and echidna we have animals surviving in a land with few large predatory carnivores. Both of them, by the nature of their diet, can rely on an abundant supply of food, the one by reason of a lack of serious aquatic competitors, the other by the great abundance of the insects on which it feeds. Added to this, platypus is not a conspicuous animal by reason of its keeping mainly to water and burrowing in the banks of the streams. In other words, it keeps very much to itself, and animals that do this tend to go unmolested. Moreover, leading a relatively solitary existence it is less likely to be subject to epidemics of disease such as are apt to afflict gregarious species. And in so far as it shows a degree of parental care, it tends to ensure a favourably low mortality in its offspring. Echidna likewise is not conspicuous, is well protected by its spines and by its ability to burrow quickly, is relatively solitary and also shows a reasonable degree of parental care. We have no evidence that there may not have been related species, having these same characteristics, that have become extinct. Indeed, by analogy, it is reasonable to suppose that there may have been such species and that their remains may yet be found, although even if this should happen it would not be possible to reconstruct their natural history sufficiently to prove that they were solitary, cared for their young, and so on. Nevertheless, look at the problem how we will, it seems that in none of these things, nor in all of them collectively, shall we necessarily find the explanation for their continued survival.

CHAPTER IV

MUSEUM OF ANTIQUE MAMMALS

THE monotremes represent a very small, but highly interesting, part of the living fossils found in Australia. Alongside them we have a wealth of other survivors in the marsupials. These are so numerous in genera and species that they compel us to look upon the continent of Australia as a portion of the past handed down more or less intact, a museum of antique mammals. First then, we need to see what the marsupials are and how they stand in relation to the mammals of the rest of the world. As compared with the monotremes they represent a step forward in the evolution of the mammals, in that they have fewer reptilian characters. They do not, for example, lay eggs. On the other hand, the young are not born in such an advanced state as those of the true or placental mammals. With this is associated the best remembered character of the marsupials, the pouch in which the later stages of the development of the young are passed. In most marsupials the pouch opens backwards, but in the kangaroos and phalangers it opens forwards. In some, however, there are merely two flaps of skin to do duty for a pouch, thus coming near to the condition found in some monotremes.

In the 230 species of living marsupials we find a sufficient number of primitive features to suggest that the group as a whole diverged early from the main mammalian stem, somewhere in the late Cretaceous. On the other hand, living marsupials have so many specialised characters that they must be looked upon as a side branch of the main stem rather than representing a stage in the evolution of the higher mammals. The skeleton as a whole shows a similar architecture to that

of the placental mammals, but the skull has a number of
primitive features, notably the incomplete condition of the
inner portion of the bony palate, the absence of an auditory
bulla, the absence of a post-orbital bar, and so on. The brain
is, however, decidedly reptilian. The cerebral hemispheres are
small and are not prolonged backwards over the cerebellum;
and the olfactory bulbs are large, the cerebellum is small, and
the internal structure of the brain is much simpler than that of
the higher mammals and nearer that of the reptile. As in the
monotremes there is a common urinogenital cloaca.

It is, however, in the embryonic development that the group
is most obviously marked off from the placental mammals.
The ovum is moderately heavily yolked and covered with an
albumen, the whole being enclosed within a membrane. It is,
in fact, a sort of soft-shelled egg, which is retained within the
uterus for the early stages, for there is, usually, no connection
between the developing embryo and the maternal tissues. In a
few marsupials, there is, nevertheless, some contact between
the wall of the yolk sac and the wall of the uterus, and in the
bandicoot there is some absorption of nourishment from the
uterine wall. The early stages in the evolution of placental
mammals is, therefore, foreshadowed, and taking the marsupials
as a whole there is seen a transition from the egg-laying of
the monotremes to the placental development of the higher
mammals.

Apart from the clues afforded by their anatomy and method
of reproduction, the Australian mammals are instructive in
giving us in simple and striking form an example of what
Osborn, the American mammalogist, called adaptive radiation. This is so marked a feature of the higher invertebrates
and of the vertebrates as to take on the character of a law. The
branching out from a main stem of a number of types each
adapted to a particular mode of life is found to some extent in
groups of species, but is more marked in groups of genera,
families, and, in a more emphatic way, in even higher groups,
such as orders, classes and phyla. It is, in fact, no more than

the rocket or tree similes put in more precise terms. And in the marsupials of Australia we see something in the nature of a natural experiment in adaptive radiation. In earlier times, as the fossil remains show, marsupials were more widespread over the earth. Some still remain in America, as we shall see in a later chapter. It would seem, furthermore, that those which reached Australia did so prior to its separation from the other land-masses, and have been able to radiate adaptively without interference from the more advanced placental mammals that succeeded them and replaced them in other parts of the world. Thus, we are presented with a very clear picture of this particular form of evolution.

Although we are accustomed to speaking of the Australian marsupials as if they formed a homogeneous group, they are, in fact, divisible into two main stocks, known respectively as the Polyprotodontia and the Diprotodontia. The first group, the name of which means literally many simple teeth, include mainly the carnivorous and insectivorous types. They are characterised by numerous small front teeth, and comprise the dasyures, thylacines and pouched mice of Australia, as well as the true opossums of America. The Diprotodontia have fewer and larger front teeth, recalling those of the rodents among placental mammals, and include the herbivorous and fruit-eating types, among them the kangaroos, wallabies, possums,* phalangers, koalas and wombats.

Attention has often been drawn to the similarity of types found in the Australian marsupials and in the placental mammals found elsewhere in the world. In other words, to the similarity in the adaptive radiations of the two groups, each with its herbivores, its carnivores, its fruit-eaters, its insectivores, as well as its running, burrowing, climbing, aquatic and flying types. In the Polyprotodontia we have, for example, the counterparts of mice, rats, cats, dogs, even jerboas. The smallest of these, the marsupial mice, with tapered shrew-like

---

* The custom has recently grown up of referring to the Australian opossums as possums, to make for easy distinction with the American or true opossums.

snouts, are common over most of Australia and range from a small mouse to a rat in size. One, the fat-tailed marsupial mouse, is able to lay up a store of fat in its tail against periods of scarcity, a physiological trick better known in several of the placental mammals. Another parallel between the marsupials and the placentals is seen in the brush-tailed marsupial rat with its grey coat and bushy tail. It is active, squirrel-like and lives in trees. (Incidentally, it is very destructive to poultry.) The smallest of the marsupials, the narrow-footed marsupial mice, live under stones and logs, feeding on insects, house mice, lizards and the like. In them there is a strong similarity to the smaller placental mammals, and especially to the shrews and moles, and like them the active marsupial mice eat more than their own body-weight of food in a day.

The jerboa-marsupials of the interior of Australia are closely related to the marsupial mice and look very like the jerboas of Africa and Asia. They have the same hind-legs and long tufted tails. And they live in burrows. It is of interest to note, and especially as our theme is living fossils, that the jerboa-marsupials were first put on record by the famous Australian naturalist Gould, in 1865. After that nothing more was seen of them, and it was supposed that they had become extinct until, nearly a century later, in 1943, they were found again, by a schoolgirl, in New South Wales.

The dasyures, or native cats, have nothing in common with the wild cats of the northern hemisphere except their carnivorous habits, which result in their persecution for raids on poultry. It is realised now, however, that they are natural enemies of the mice, rats and rabbits that have, unhappily, been introduced. Although reduced in numbers they would stand a good chance of re-establishing themselves if left unmolested, for an unusual reason which amounts to a biological paradox. It is that, whereas the female dasyure may have as many as twenty-four young at a birth, she has only six teats to feed them. The least we can say of such extravagant procreation is that it ensures that each teat shall be used to the full.

16. THE NATIVE CAT OF AUSTRALIA has little in common with the domestic cat except its carnivorous habits.

The dog-like type is represented by the thylacine or Tasmanian wolf. Three feet long in the body, with the hind parts marked with dark bands, it has a long tail and a dog-like head, and does, indeed, look very like a dog. The female has, however, the pouch typical of her race, and the skull although superficially dog-like preserves the marsupial peculiarities, particularly in the number of the teeth. The thylacine was formerly living on the mainland but is now confined to Tasmania. Even there it is rare, and those who have gone out specially equipped to track it down have very seldom succeeded. Although its tracks were found the animal itself escaped observation. Even by putting down traps, with the intention, it should be stated, of catching the beast alive and releasing it after establishing its presence, its trackers had no success. The question remains, therefore, whether the thylacine is going down in a natural decline, or whether, as is usually assumed, it has suffered from the introduction of the dingo. It has also been persecuted by man, and especially by the early

17. THYLACINE OR TASMANIAN WOLF, largest of the
carnivorous marsupials. Once common in Australia,
it now survives in small numbers in Tasmania.

white settlers, which may have a good deal to do with its
disappearance. The reason for its persecution by man was that,
although its natural food is wallabies, rats and birds, dog-like
it started to kill sheep and poultry. The thylacine has legs of
equal length and normally moves like any other quadruped so
proportioned, but it has been reported by several observers
that when chased hard it will bound in the manner of a
kangaroo. Such behaviour is difficult to relate to the general
story of the evolution of the marsupials, and may be explained
only when more is known of marsupial fossils.

Not only are there the counterparts of mice, rats, jerboas,
cats and dogs among the Polyprotodontia, there are also
anteaters and moles. The banded anteater, of south and south-
west Australia, is about the size of a rat. In common with a
number of other mammals, belonging to different groups of
placentals, which feed largely on ants and termites, it has a

18. THE MARSUPIAL MOLE of the Central Australian deserts shows a remarkable resemblance to early arthropods.

tapering snout and long extensile tongue for feeding on termites, which it digs out of rotten wood with its strong claws. The marsupial mole is, in some ways, the most outstanding of the marsupials in supporting Osborn's hypothesis. It is not merely burrowing; it has also attained the high degree of specialisation to a subterranean life seen in the true moles and the mole rats, among the placentals. The marsupial mole escaped detection, so far as the scientific world is concerned, until 1888. It lives in the sandy ground of south, central and north-west Australia, burrowing about three inches below the surface. Further, it is without eyes or eyelids, or external ears, and the snout is peculiar in that it is protected by a horny shield. The fore-limbs, too, are more strongly developed and each bears a pair of prominent claws, and the cervical vertebrae are fused; but otherwise, the marsupial mole is very like the European mole, especially in its restless activity and its enormous appetite.

To continue cataloguing the Polyprotodontia: the bandicoots are rabbit-like, but while feeding mainly on vegetation they also eat insects. Although still abundant in places, they are less numerous than formerly. The commonest is the long-nosed bandicoot, about the size of a small rabbit, with a spiny coat of stiff fur. It feeds mainly on earthworms and insect grubs, digging small pits in its search for them, and, as might be expected, it has incurred the displeasure of those who see their gardens and lawns damaged by its activities. On the other hand, it will also take mice, and it has the curious trick of pummelling them into a shapeless mass before eating. Another interesting parallel, this time with the mole, is seen in its method of eating earthworms, passing them through the fingers before consuming them. Finally, it is worth noting that, in contrast to the female dasyure, the female bandicoot has only two to four young at a birth but has eight teats with which to feed them. Since both in dasyures and bandicoots the numbers showed no adverse trend apart from human interference, it seems that discrepancies between the numbers of young produced at a birth and the means of feeding them can have little effect on the survival of the species as a whole.

The rabbit bandicoot, so-called from its large rabbit-like ears, shows an even greater reduction in numbers than the long-nosed bandicoot, due to having been killed for its fur, and also because it is preyed upon by foxes imported into Australia. It lives in burrows having only one exit, but compensating for this it has the ability to burrow rapidly, as fast as a man can dig, which gives it a ready defence against natural enemies. Another peculiarity, which has no bearing on survival although interesting in itself, is the sleeping position adopted by the rabbit bandicoot, squatting on its haunches with the snout tucked between the fore-paws and the ears folded on themselves.

The Diprotodontia, including possums, phalangers, koalas, wombats, wallabies and kangaroos, all live on a mainly vegetarian diet. In addition to the form of the front teeth, the hind-foot has a peculiar structure, the first toe being absent, the second and third bound together in a common skin, and the fourth and fifth variable in size from one species to another. Thus, in the kangaroos and wallabies, the fourth and fifth toes are long, but in the phalangers they are short and armed with curved claws so that they form a grasping organ. They are the functional toes—markedly so in kangaroos and wallabies—the second and third, looking like one toe with a pair of claws at the end, being used for combing the fur.

The first family of Diprotodontia includes the possums, phalangers, cuscuses and the koala, in all of which the fore-legs and hind-legs are not markedly different in size. Except in the koala, all have the pouch opening forward. All live in trees and, again the koala excepted, have prehensile tails. And linked with the arboreal life, all have the big toe opposable to the rest, for grasping. They feed on leaves, fruit, flowers, and, in some cases, on honey or insects. The small honey mouse, for example, an animal seldom seen because of its nocturnal habits, and known largely because domestic cats frequently bring it in, feeds largely on nectar. It does, however, eat insects, discarding the heads, wings and legs, which is the more surprising since, correlated with a main diet of nectar, the teeth are very small, and apparently of little use. As in certain other nectar-eating mammals, such as the long-tongued bats of south-east Asia, and the birds known as honey-suckers, of Australia, New Guinea and Polynesia, it has a long extensile tongue armed with bristles for brushing up the nectar from flowers.

The specialised habits of the honey mouse can be contrasted with the versatility, or adaptability, of the brush-tailed possum, formerly known as the vulpine opossum, which lives on the eucalyptus and is found wherever this tree grows. It is the size of a fox, with a fox-like head, large ears and a bushy tail. It has a thick woolly fur, silver-grey to dark brown and black in colour, forming a pelt much in demand by the fur trade, with the result that a very large number of skins is exported each year. Although its natural home is in the trees, it can thrive equally well in the low bush, and will even make its home in rabbit warrens, or in the roof spaces in suburban houses. The brushtail has also been successfully introduced into New Zealand.

Another tree-dwelling marsupial is the striped phalanger, about the size of a squirrel, living only in the forests of Northern

Queensland, with related species in New Guinea. Striped black and white, this phalanger recalls in its habits the aye-aye of Madagascar, one of the lemurs. The fourth toe of its front foot, like the third toe of the aye-aye, is long and thin and used for hooking insects and larvae out of rotten wood. The phalanger drums on the bark with its fore-feet to disturb the grubs, rips up the wood with its powerful incisors and then runs this sensitive finger in to pick out the grubs.

The Australian marsupials include also some that have developed the "volant" habit. These are the so-called flying phalangers. The smallest of these is the delicately built pygmy flying phalanger of the eucalyptus forests of eastern Australia and New Guinea. It nests in holes in trees and is able to make gliding flights from tree to tree. But instead of the gliding membrane usually found in animals of this habit there is a fringe of stiff hairs running along the sides of the body, and these serve the same purpose. The tail, as is usually the case in gliding mammals, is feather-like. The real gliding phalangers, that is, those with a web of skin on either side of the body to keep them airborne, spend the day-time resting in holes in the trees, coming out at night to make long gliding leaps. One of the great gliders, the largest of these phalangers, about the size of a cat, has been seen to cover a third of a mile in six successive glides from tree to tree. The price of this specialised habit is to make the gliding phalangers slow and clumsy on the ground, but they are moderately safe from human persecution, not only on account of their nocturnal habits, and from the fact that, feeding on leaves, they do not come into conflict with human interests, but also because their fur is too fine and soft to be of use in commerce. The main danger for them, as for so many arboreal animals, lies in the possible destruction of the forests as human settlement advances.

Ring-tailed possums, of Australia and New Guinea, are also arboreal, living in holes in trees, where they build nests like squirrels. They too are nocturnal; and their long tails can be coiled into a ring for grasping branches. In the largest of

19. THE PYGMY GLIDER, the smallest marsupial
capable of gliding leaps, the feather-like tail forming
an effective rudder.

the possums, the cuscuses, the end half of the tail is naked and
scaly, giving a much firmer grasp. Cuscuses look very like
monkeys, and have been responsible for reports circulating
from time to time of the supposed discovery of monkeys in the
forests of New Guinea, Celebes, the Solomon Islands and
Queensland, Australia. Of the sixteen or so species, two only
are found in Queensland. Cuscuses are strongly and heavily
built, slow-moving, and spend most of the day coiled up in the
forks of trees or in travelling slowly about consuming large
quantities of leaves, which with fruits, large insects, even birds
and their eggs, make up their diet. About the size of a large cat,
measuring three feet or more, including the long tail, the body
of a cuscus is covered with a woolly coat. The likeness to a
monkey is enhanced by the rounded face.

Cuscuses are highly specialised for their particular way of
life and seldom survive long in captivity. They are presumably

not adaptable, therefore, but in their own environment they enjoy several natural advantages. The coat is an effective protection against all weathers; and their vicious disposition and sharp claws, as well as the skunk-like habit of using an evil-smelling excretion, gives them a moderate freedom from natural enemies. The python is their chief enemy, although, as David Fleay, the Australian naturalist puts it:

> Odour notwithstanding, natives relish Cuscus flesh, and, catching their victims with ease, owing to the marsupial's slow movements in the trees, they set to work with primitive directness, unhampered by any susceptibilities, and immediately break their victim's legs. By this means escape of the animal and deterioration of its flesh are prevented until such time as it is needed for cooking.

Probably the most highly specialised of all Australia's marsupials is the koala, the so-called Australian Teddy Bear, a small, brown bear-like animal, about two feet high, with tufted ears and a prominent beak-like snout. It also lives in eucalyptus trees, feeding on the leaves, and its diet is among the most specialised in the animal kingdom. It is said that koalas of one area transported into another area do not readily get used to the leaves of the gum trees native to their new home. In fact, it has been said that the leaves of one district may actually prove poisonous to koalas from another district. If this is true, it cannot be generally so. It may relate to certain individuals, or even to certain districts, for koalas have been moved from their native haunts and have survived such transportation. Nevertheless, it serves to emphasise the highly specialised nature of the diet, and clearly the koala could not survive the extinction of the eucalyptus.

Koalas must be almost without a rival for gentleness of disposition, and their charms are in no way diminished by the picture of the female carrying her usually single offspring pick-a-back when it is old enough to leave the pouch. On the other hand, the demands of the fur trade have caused a sad

20. SPOTTED CUSCUS, a large tree-dwelling phalanger.

thinning of its ranks, and in some parts of Australia it has been wiped out. In 1924, for example, over two million koala skins were exported, and this, with the clearing of the forests, has brought the animal to the point where steps have had to be taken to protect it.

Finally, we have to consider the best known, and the first discovered, of the Australian marsupials, the kangaroos and wallabies. Captain Cook is usually given the credit for this discovery, but although he described the large leaping animals, called Kangaru—or so he believed—by the natives, at Cook-town, in Queensland, in 1770, it was the Dutchman Pelsart who, in 1629, when wrecked on the Abrolhos Islands off the south-west of Australia, saw what is now called the dama wallaby. He wrote an account of this strange beast, and described the method of carrying the young in the pouch. He was, however, misled into thinking that the young were born in the pouch. The best definition that can be given of a wallaby is that it is a small kangaroo; of a kangaroo, that it is

a large wallaby. Certain stockily built kangaroos are known
as wallaroos. So it happens that the use of the names kangaroo
and wallaby varies from place to place, with the result that
some wallabies are bigger than certain species normally referred
to as kangaroos, and some species referred to as kangaroos are
smaller than the largest wallabies.

Not all the kangaroos and wallabies are large. There are,
for example, a number of rat-kangaroos, usually no larger
than rabbits, and like them living among low vegetation and
sometimes in shallow burrows. They are less noticeably built
for jumping, and at best hop rather than leap. And some do
not do even this. Nevertheless, where they move about on all
fours, they do sit up on their hindquarters to feed. The hare
wallabies, on the other hand, are not only the size of hares but
compare with them in speed of movement and agility.

Other groups of kangaroos (or wallabies) are named according to their habitats. The tree kangaroos, two to three feet high,
of northern Queensland and New Guinea, may be brightly
coloured orange or yellow. Although they ascend the trees
to feed and to sleep, they also spend much of their time on the
ground. Where a leisurely descent is possible, they come down
from the trees tail first, but if in a hurry to escape, they may leap
anything up to fifty feet to the ground.

The rock wallabies are quite like the tree kangaroos in
appearance and size, but they inhabit the barren rock-strewn
gullies, feeding on leaves and fruit. The soles of their hind-feet
are padded and granulated, facilitating movement over the
smooth slippery surfaces of the rocks. As in tree kangaroos, the
fur is often brightly coloured, an unfortunate circumstance,
for the ring-tailed rock wallaby is in danger of extinction from
being hunted for its valuable pelt. Rock wallabies have the
usual mild and inoffensive disposition of the herbivore, but
they are not incapable of defending themselves, their tactics
being to close with an enemy, whom they grasp with the short
front legs while striking viciously with the claws of the
hind-feet.

21. THE KANGAROO, the largest and best-known
Australian marsupial, specially built for leaping.

The scrub or pademelon wallabies, of small size compared
with the more familiar kangaroos, and with somewhat short
tails, live in the long grass or dense undergrowth, making
tunnel-like runways recalling those made by rabbits. This
constant reference to small and seemingly insignificant
comparisons with the placental mammals is not without point,
for it serves to underline the completeness of the parallels in
adaptive radiation. There is a further comparison worthy of
mention. A scrub wallaby in the face of a threat of danger will,
like the rabbit, thump on the ground with its hind-feet,
serving to warn the rest. And this is a feature, moreover, of all
kangaroos (or wallabies) that are gregarious.

The marsupials so far considered conform to three of the
five classes enumerated by later writers on adaptive radiation.
We have had climbing, burrowing and flying, if gliding be
so interpreted. There have been no aquatic marsupials in

Australia, although there is the water opossum in South
America, but presumably this can be accounted for on the
grounds that that particular ecological niche has been exploited
by the monotreme platypus. There have also been the cursorial
types, as, for example, the hare wallabies; but the full expression
of a cursorial type is seen in the larger kangaroos, and for our
examples we need not go further than the large grey and red
kangaroos, the last of these being the most widespread of the
larger marsupials. Although these large kangaroos are capable
of speed and leaping powers, there has been a tendency to
exaggerate their performances in both. When accurate measurements are taken, it seems that the fastest kangaroo, over flat
country, does not exceed 25 miles an hour over a 300-yard
stretch, possibly on occasion 30 miles an hour, whereas
antelope and deer may attain 50 miles an hour. As to leaping,
a long jump of 26 feet is very near the maximum of which
even the largest kangaroos are capable, and this is a little
better than the achievement of a human athlete. Also, it is not
remarkable compared with the performances of some of the
ungulates, among placental mammals. Moreover, kangaroos
usually clear little more than 5 feet, and some have become
entangled and maimed by fences of this height, although there
is a record of one having cleared a 9-foot fence. Even so, they
form the counterpart among the placental mammals of the
grazing and browsing herbivores, relying on speed of movement for security. If the present-day marsupials are a fair sample
of marsupials of the past, we can understand that they should
have failed to survive elsewhere in any numbers in face of the
evolution of the large placental carnivores. Proof of this on a
local scale is seen in the ravages made in Australia among the
smaller marsupials by the imported foxes.

Whether the marsupials can be called living fossils in the
strict sense, or whether, indeed, the monotremes can be so-called
is a matter of opinion. Rather they are the specialised survivors
of an ancient stock which diverged from the main mammalian
stem early in its history. What we should expect, therefore,

is that some marsupials are more primitive than others, some more deserving of the name living fossil. It is, however, customary to treat them as a group of living fossils. However we regard them, they do give us valuable clues concerning the origin of mammals from a reptilian stock, and they afford a striking example of the principle of adaptive radiation and its place in the total process of evolution. There is, moreover, one more important lesson or group of lessons to be drawn from the Australian mammals, on the possible causes of extinction, and by inverting these, of survival. We can emphasise, by the examples found in the Australian fauna, the danger of over-specialisation—most obvious in the tree-dwelling forms—by being closely tied to a particular habitat. With the destruction, or even the diminution of the forests, which could happen from natural causes such as changes in climate, such species are in danger of extinction or of reduction to numbers where a concatenation of minor adverse circumstances could effect extinction. By contrast, we can see in the brush-tailed possum the advantages of adaptability, of being able to make use of a wide variety of habitats. Its adaptability is also seen in the success with which it has been introduced into New Zealand.

Another form of specialisation concerns the diet, and here the outstanding example is the koala. With destruction of forests, as postulated in the previous paragraph, a species so closely tied to one type of food would be brought to the verge of extinction, unless some of its individuals, showing a greater physiological latitude, or adaptability, were able to survive by taking to another food plant. This would lead, however, in all probability to the ultimate emergence of one or more new species.

A sidelight is thrown also on the role of the predator in the extinction of species. Thus, it is usually assumed that the thylacine was exterminated on the mainland of Australia by the introduction of the dingo. In other words, dog was eating (marsupial) dog. If this be true, are we to suppose that the extinction of the thylacine was due to direct attack or to competition for food? The latter can surely be ruled out in a large land-mass so abundantly supplied with small mammals, of which the majority had little means of protecting themselves against a powerful and active carnivore, even when it was only a marsupial carnivore. At best, we can say that extinction may have been brought about by the introduction of a new and powerful predator into an otherwise balanced economy under exceptional circumstances. At the worst, it proves nothing at all, except the unlikely event that one predator ousts another, even in the presence of abundant food. And from this, and from other deductions, it seems more reasonable to suppose that the thylacine was already in decline and first the dingo, and then man, hastened its departure.

The more likely explanation, then, to my mind, is that the thylacine was already in decline; and if the existence of a larger marsupial carnivore, the so-called wild cat of Queensland (*see* page 263) has any foundation in fact, then we are probably in the presence of another and larger relative of the thylacine, in which decline has advanced still further. This would be very much in line with what we shall see again and again in other species. In conjunction with these things, we may recall also reports of giant kangaroos in out-of-the-way places in Australia, none of which has been confirmed by evidence acceptable to science. Nevertheless, this, too, would be in keeping with the general picture, if we could suppose that they represented the last remnants of a much larger species, few in numbers, that had retreated to inaccessible places. Fossil remains have been found of marsupials larger than any living today, and it is not unreasonable to suppose that if the geological record for Australia were more complete, we should find there, as elsewhere, indications of a gigantism preceding a decline in certain of the lines of evolution represented by modern marsupials. In the absence of evidence to the contrary, it is reasonable to postulate that the—at present mythical—large thylacine-like wild cat, and the thylacine itself, represent the end stages of a declining stock, and that the last few centuries have seen the final stages in the decline. Equally, it would be reasonable to suppose that the present-day large kangaroos represent a similar decline in another stock, the final demise of which is not so immediately imminent but is nevertheless in progress.

CHAPTER V

AMERICAN OPOSSUMS

PART from Australia and the islands to the north of it, the only other part of the world in which marsupials are living today is America, and there they are relatively few in number. As we have seen in greater detail in an early chapter, at the opening of the Jurassic period, when the main stem of the mammals was first beginning to develop, there existed in the tropical and southern regions of the globe a continental land-mass which has been named Gondwanaland. This is believed to have extended from South America across what is now Africa and the Indian Ocean to Australia. One hundred million years later, by the Eocene period, the same evidence suggests that South America, Africa and Australia were each separated by wide seas, and with other changes to the north the continents were beginning to assume the form familiar to us today.

The surviving marsupials of the American continent belong exclusively to the Polyprotodontia. They include two families peculiar to America, the Didelphidae, or true opossums of America, and the Coenolestidae, containing very few species. The true opossums include the common opossum, famous for its habit of feigning death when its safety is threatened, lying apparently lifeless and with its hair dishevelled. It was to describe this trick that the phrase "playing possum" was early coined. It is of interest to see, therefore, the abbreviated form of the word—that is, "possum"—being brought into current use, not for the American species but for those resident in Australia. This is not, however, the end of the story, for in 1952 Dr. Carl G. Hartman, of the U.S.A., published a book dealing with the marsupials, which included an exhaustive survey of the American varieties. He entitled his book ... *Possums*.

It may not be unprofitable, and it certainly is not without interest, to see what Dr. Hartman has to say about the origins of the name. Thus: "... it was Captain John Smith who wrote the first description in English of the 'Virginia' opossum and bestowed upon it the Indian name, *opossum*, by which it is now known". And later in the book: ". . . John Brickell, M.D., the King's surveyor in Carolina, tells us that the word actually was *possum*, but that this was preceded by a grunt, hence the *o-opossum*". Moreover, he shows how from 1612 until 1787, the name has been set forth by various writers in ten other variations, *opassom*, *ouassom*, *opussum*, and so on. We can say this, at least, for the present day, that if there is still some confusion, we are approaching something like stability in usage. The name itself means "white animal", in reference to the white face of the Virginian opossum.

Dr. Hartman also points out that:

The first name for the opossum to be printed in books was invented by Gesner in 1558. One would think that, since the pouch was the sensational feature of the new discovery, the name would have been based on that character, as indeed it was later: Marsupalia, from the Latin *marsupium*, "pouch". But Gesner, reading Peter Martyr's original 1516 description—half monkey, half fox—came up with *simivulpa* or *simia vulpina*, "fox-monkey" in English, *Fuchsaffe* in German. Aldrovandi, "the Italian Gesner", also used *simivulpa* as well as *vulpisimia* . . .

To return to America, an opossum was first brought to the notice of Europeans by Vicente Yáñez Pinzón, who captained one of Columbus' caravels, and later led his own expeditions to the new-found continent. It was on his return from one of these, in 1500, that he brought back an opossum and presented it at the court of Ferdinand of Spain. It was not until 1793 that the name was given to the Australian marsupials, by Captain John Hunter, in his *Historical Journal*. Writing of the animals he had seen in New South Wales, he says: "The opossum is also numerous here, but it is not exactly like the American opossum; it partakes a good deal of the kangaroo in the strength of its tail and make of its forefeet . . ."

The first American opossum to be brought to Europe was not the Virginian or common opossum, however, for Pinzón obtained his "specimen" from Brazil. But it is the one best-known to us in the literature. It is about the size of a domestic cat, with the body about twenty inches long, and a naked scaly tail, about a foot long; it is the largest of the American opossums. The snout is long and tapering, somewhat rat-like, the body is covered with grey fur composed of a soft underfur and long bristle-like guard hairs. It is these last, more especially, that give the dishevelled effect when the beast is feigning dead. Living in trees, it holds on with its prehensile tail and its grasping feet, the large toe being opposable to the rest. It is nocturnal, sleeping by day in a hollow tree, or among the branches, or under a log. Its diet includes almost anything edible, especially fruit, insects, eggs, reptiles including snakes, small birds and small mammals. The five to fourteen young— and there are two to three litters a year—are barely half an inch long and in an undeveloped condition when born, as in all marsupials. They make their way to the pouch, each becoming attached to a teat; and at a later stage, when able to move about freely, they leave the pouch to climb on to the mother's back, returning to it for food and shelter.

The Didelphidae, although now confined to the Americas, formerly ranged over Europe as well, their fossils being found there in the Eocene deposits. Like the Australian possums they have a well-developed, nailless, opposable first toe, but are distinguished mainly by the more numerous incisors, there being five in the upper jaw (each side) and four in the lower jaw as against four and three respectively in the Australian possums. The pouch, not always present, is often no more than

22. THE COMMON OPOSSUM of America feigning death: a survivor from the past that has given us the well-known phrase "playing 'possum'".

a pair of folds of the abdominal skin. Otherwise, the American opossums have many of the primitive features associated with the Australian opossums, including the small and relatively simple brain; taking all things into consideration, there is every reason to regard them as more archaic even than their Australian relatives.

The South American species of Didelphidae are fairly numerous, and all are smaller than the common opossum. Their outward appearance, as might be expected, differs a little from that of the Australian species. They include, for example, the rat-tailed opossum, about the size of a rat, with a long naked tail, a black and white face and a black streak running down the back. The woolly opossum is about the size of a squirrel and has a bushy tail. The thick-tailed opossum, of Uruguay, Paraguay and the Argentine, is coloured a yellow ochre and has a thick tapering tail, black with white at the tip. One species, *Monodelphys domesticus*, lives in the native huts, having the same commensal relation to these dwellings that the house mouse has to our buildings. Its tail is short and is not prehensile; in a related species, *Notodelphys halli*, the tail is both short and fat. The genus *Marmosa* includes a large number of species with long naked tails and dark markings round the eyes, ranging from the size of mice to that of rats. One species looks very like the dormouse, and another, related, species recalls the dormouse even more since, just before entering its period of summer sleep, it lays in a store of fat, though it does so around the tail.

The water opossum ranges from Guatemala, in Central America, to Brazil in the south. It is rat-sized, with a long white-tipped scaly tail. Its hind-feet are large and webbed. Its coat is soft, recalling that of the otter, an animal it also resembles in its aquatic habits and methods of feeding. In appearance, however, it recalls the thylacine, for its body is marked with alternate bands of a dark chocolate colour and a dirty white, with white underparts. The philander opossums, of which there are numerous species distributed over Central and South America, are about two feet long, more than half of which is taken up by the naked white-tipped tail. They are the more brightly coloured species, often a brilliant orange above and grey below, with the face marked with orange eye-stripes and a black stripe along the middle of the head.

All the American opossums considered so far fall naturally into one family. There is another, a shrew-like insectivorous marsupial, living in the dark humid forests of the higher Andes, known as *Coenolestes*, since it has no common name. It is peculiar in having the teeth of a Diprotodont and the foot of a Polyprotodont. The Gordian knot is cut in this instance by placing it in a family of its own, the Coenolestidae.

To understand the significance of the surviving South American marsupials they must be examined in terms of adaptive radiation, construed in its widest terms. In reviewing

23. THE WATER OPOSSUM OR YAPOK of South America, web-footed and scaly-tailed, the only aquatic marsupial.

the Australian mammals, attention was drawn to Osborn's notion of an adaptive radiation, in which is postulated a fivefold radiation from a main stem. It was found that the marsupials of Australia fully conform to this except that they lack an aquatic form, which is probably supplied by the platypus. Among placental mammals, these five radiations are more conspicuously seen. The cursorial, or running animals, are represented by deer, sheep, the carnivores, and many others. The fossorial, or burrowing, show to best advantage in the moles. There is no lack of climbing animals, nor aquatic; indeed, in almost every order of the placentals these are well represented, and the volant or flying types are represented by a whole order, the bats, as well as several groups belonging to other orders in which gliding has been brought to an efficient pitch of development. The same may be said of the class Aves, or birds, except that in them the emphasis is on flying, though all other activities are well represented notwithstanding. In reptiles we have a similar radiation, except that modern reptiles of the volant group include only gliding species. Nevertheless, in former times, when the reptiles were at the height of their development, they included the pterodactyls. The amphibia run true to this same pattern, even to gliding frogs, although nothing like true flight has been developed.

Always, in biology, what appears at first to be a general law tends to break down in its wider application, or needs to be hedged in at some points with qualifications. As applied strictly to land animals, the law, if it can be so called, of adaptive radiation, holds fairly steadily true. Among the invertebrates, then, the only truly terrestrial groups are the insects, spiders and the myriapods, and in the first two of these the five lines of adaptive radiation can be seen, with flight most prominently developed in insects and confined in spiders ". . . to parachuting on silken threads. It is possible also to see the law in force among the other groups of invertebrates, those like the crustacea and mollusca, which are mainly aquatic, as well as among those which have no representatives on land; though it must be admitted that the myriapods (millipedes and centipedes) prove an awkward exception."

If we confine attention, however, to terrestrial animals, to which Osborn's concept is intended more particularly to apply, then we can embrace wider implications of the law of adaptive radiation. We can, in fact, use it as a measure of the development, almost of the age, of any group of animals at a given point in time, and this can be applied not only to phyla, classes and orders, but even to families, and possibly genera. Let us imagine the emergence of a primitive, generalised type. Speaking in terms of terrestrial animals, we can suppose it merely living on the ground, so to speak, taking what food it can reach and using such shelter as is immediately available. In the course of time, its descendants begin to show varying structure and qualities, and this, combined with the everlasting search for living space carries them, each according to its equipment, into different ecological niches. As this group, whether phylum, class, order or family reaches the full flush of development, its offshoots will have explored and settled in every type of habitat, giving us cursorial, fossorial, scansorial, aquatic and volant types. As the group, phylum, class or what it be, passes maturity and goes into decline, the dying out will not take place evenly and one line of radiation will tend to disappear before the others. So, at a later stage, when the decline has already set in, the volant types may have disappeared, or even the scansorial, and so on. At a given period in time, then, we can judge, at least approximately, the "age" of a group by the range of habitats occupied by its members, in terms so to speak of fifths.

Mention has been made of the absence of volant, and possibly other types in the Myriapoda, which represent, nevertheless, a major group in our classificatory series. As we shall see in a later chapter, the millipedes and centipedes comprising this class belong to an archaic race, with a long history in time. Their fossil remains are numerous, so that we have a fairly complete record; yet nowhere do we find evidence of a volant type of myriapod. The fossil record is, however, largely a record of structure and of the structure of the hard parts at that. In some instances there is preserved more or less of the soft parts, usually in the form of impressions. Something can also be deduced of the structure of the soft parts, by comparison with what is found in living animals. It is even possible to build up in some instances a fairly complete account of the embryology and development, and in general terms it is possible to deduce something of the habits of a particular animal, whether it was herbivorous or carnivorous, and so on. Yet, when all is said and done, the palaeontological record is of the structure of the hard parts and relatively little more. Who, seeing the skeleton of a water chevrotain, for example, which is the skeleton of a typical cursorial animal, would imagine that it spent much of its time in water and could "swim like a duck" and dive with something of the efficiency of a seal? Or, again, who, confronted with the remains of a spider perfectly preserved in the rock, or even in amber,

7

and having no other evidence to go upon, would guess that it was capable at some stage in its lifetime of spreading silken threads into the wind and remaining airborne for long periods? So, with the myriapods, the possibility cannot be excluded that there may have been a volant, or any other type in the past.

All this is taking the concept of adaptive radiation beyond what it normally implies, but it seems to me we can take it even further. In this discussion I have suggested that the measure of maturity of a group, of its youth or decline, can be approximately gauged by the degree to which its members occupy the five adaptively radiating lines. In it, the suggestion has been made that this is true of phyla, classes, orders, families, and, possibly, even genera. In a sense the concept of adaptive radiation can be applied to species, even to the individuals.

At every step, the history and behaviour of the larger groups of animals challenge comparison with those of individuals. Whether such comparisons are apparent rather than real may ultimately be a matter of opinion. At this stage, however, it is at least necessary to examine the materials upon which such comparisons could be made. It has been found inevitable to speak of the youth, maturity and decline of large groups, such as phyla and classes. Osborn, in putting forward his idea of adaptive radiation has implied, in broad terms, a group adaptability. The course of adaptive radiation follows a course closely comparable with certain features of the lifetime of an individual. In the beginning there is energy and enterprise. In the large groupings, this takes the form of an increase in range, territorially or geographically, and an active proliferation of species, genera and families, an expansion and an exploration. Then the group, like an individual, reaches its prime; after which it goes into a steady decline. Its range tends to decrease, certain of its branches die out or atrophy; it withdraws into itself and is no longer capable of fresh endeavours or explorations.

When we come to apply these ideas to a species, the first obstacle lies in the impossibility of knowing how far a given species may be considered young or old, in the ascendant, at its prime or in its decline. Two examples present themselves, however, which at the least suggest how the concept of adaptive radiation could be applied to a species. The starling of western Europe has, in the last century, considerably extended its range, even within its native territories. Where it has been introduced outside these territories, as in North America, for example, its spread and the increases in its populations have been little short of phenomenal. It is always possible to point to the abundance of food provided by the increase of arable land in recent times, the increased provision of shelter and, especially, of nesting sites by the spread of human habitations, and the reduction in its natural enemies, particularly by the killing off of hawks. Even so, while all these things may have contributed to the starling's success, there seems to be a peculiar vitality behind the spread and expansion of the species. Collaterally with this, we see, even in the individual starling, an adaptability of a wide order. It will feed in grass, taking insects just below the surface. It will scavenge the surface of the ground, search the trees and take food at almost any level up to tree-top height, often hawking and hovering in a manner recalling somewhat the feeding methods of flycatchers, swallows and a variety of other species with more set habits. Its normal feeding-ground is, of course, grassland; but the point is that it can often be observed resorting to other habits, and it is not impossible to imagine a starling prevented from normal feeding turning to any one of these other methods.

In other ways, too, starlings give an appearance of unusual adaptability, noticeably in their readiness to take almost any kind of food, and, to a lesser extent, in using a variety of nesting sites. There are, of course, other factors which could account for their success as a species. These include such things as an obvious belligerence in ousting other birds from a supply of food, seen at its maximum on the feeding tray in the garden; the training of the young birds by the parents; acting in a common defence against predators; and, generally, in making use of all the advantages of an intensely gregarious habit. To sum up, we would seem to have in the starling a young species, presented with an abundance of food but with other factors contributing to its success.

A similar example is seen in the spread of the brown and the black rat. Rodents are believed to have originated in south-east Asia, and within historic times we have the record of the two spreading across Asia and Europe and concurrently increasing enormously in numbers. Their spread elsewhere must be attributed to human agency and for our present purpose must be disregarded, except to note that wherever they are introduced they flourish exceedingly. It is true that, as with starlings, there is the same provision of an abundance of food, due to prodigal human habits as well as to our methods of storing food. There has been the same reduction in the predators, the smaller carnivores, but in this instance it has been partly counter-balanced by the widespread habit of keeping domestic cats and dogs. Above all, rats are cursorial, fossorial, scansorial, aquatic, and, if we may count the taking of flying leaps, incipiently volant.

To return to America and its marsupials, it is fair to claim in the light of these discussions there is less sign among them of adaptability than among the Australian marsupials. Indeed, they appear more truly living fossils than those of Australia. They are slightly more archaic in structure, particularly in the development of the brain and the marsupium. They are all of small size, and the numbers of their species and genera are comparatively small. Since the remains of some of their ancestors attain a far greater maximum size, it must be assumed that they are in decline. And while admittedly there is much yet to be learned about the mammalian fauna of South America, there is at present no knowledge of a volant marsupial on the American continent, and none markedly fossorial, like the marsupial mole of Australia. In terms of adaptive radiation, therefore, there is a meagre three-fifths at the best.

South America, in particular, is the home of end-pieces in

evolution, although the picture of them is by no means so clear-cut as in Australia. There are two reasons for this. The zoology and the palaeontology of that region are not as fully known as are those of most regions of the globe. And the land bridge with North America, itself connected within comparatively recent times with Asia, has made possible the spread into South America of more recent types, including two of the big cats, the puma and jaguar, as well as dog-like carnivores.

Among the other archaic types, for which South and Central America are renowned, are the order Edentata of the placental mammals, the sloths, armadillos and anteaters proper. Usually placed low in the scale of the true mammals, all have become specialised, and the characteristic feature is the reduction in or total loss of the teeth. They also have a small brain with enlarged olfactory lobes, and many features of the bony skeleton must be regarded as simple or generalised and reflecting the conditions found in the early placental stock.

There are two kinds of living sloths—the three-toed, characteristic of Central America, and the two-toed of South America. They differ considerably in form, activity and temperament, but both are tree-dwelling, and markedly specialised for this; so much so, that they are at a considerable disadvantage if they find themselves on the ground. Both have only one young at a birth, which is carried clinging to the mother's hair and fed with food partly digested and regurgitated by the mother. Their specialised features do not so much concern us here, and such things as their habit of hanging upside-down from branches, clinging by their hook-like claws, the possession of grooved hairs containing unicellular plants giving an overall green appearance which make them harmonise with the foliage, are all well-known. And so is their most distinctive feature, the slowness of movement. Two things only need, therefore, be emphasised.

The first is that one of their nearest relatives was the giant ground sloth, *Megatherium*, which was nearly as large as an elephant. This became extinct so recently that remains of its skin and hair have been found in a sufficiently good state of preservation to be examined biochemically. Others, known from the Eocene and the Pleistocene of South America, that had earlier become extinct, were also large. Thus we have again the appearance of large size preceding a decline.

The other point derives from a comparison between the present-day sloths and the cuscuses. Both possess the arboreal habit to a highly specialised degree, the hook-like claws, the herbivorous diet, more pronounced in the sloths, and the slowness in movement. Indeed, so striking is the similarity between these animals, belonging to two different sub-classes and living in widely separated regions, that one must arrive at one of two conclusions. We must assume either that the sloths as a whole were formerly as numerous and as varied as the marsupials; or else that, for some reason we can but guess at, their expansion and development, even when they were at their zenith, were more circumscribed than that of the Australa-sian marsupials and other major groups.

The picture presented by the sloths is almost exactly repeated in the armadillos, with a few additional features. With one exception, armadillos are partly cursorial and partly fossorial, but the fairy armadillo, or pichiciago, six inches long, is somewhat mole-like in form and, although little is known of its habits, it is believed to be completely burrowing. The largest of the living armadillos is the giant armadillo of the Brazilian forests, three feet long from the tip of the snout to the root of the tail, with a tail twenty inches long. The remaining species are considerably smaller in size. This can be contrasted with the fossil giant armadillo, *Glyptodon*, from the Pleistocene of Argentina, which was five feet high and was over eight feet long, including the tail. With, today, barely a two-fifths adaptive radiation and extinct forms greatly exceed-ing in size those now living, with the restriction of their total range and a paucity of living species, there is every reason to regard the edentates as in decline. If so, the recent spread of the nine-banded armadillo may have a special significance.

This species ranges from the northern Argentine to Texas, Louisiana, Florida and Oklahoma, but it appears to be increasing in numbers and in its range in the U.S.A.

The nine-banded armadillo, with an average of seventeen inches, is of medium size as armadillos go today. It feeds mainly on insects or other small invertebrates, such as worms. In addition to the advantage of eating a food which an extension of arable land would make more abundant, there are other things that might favour an increase. Thus, the female carries a pair of teats on the abdomen as well as the pair normally found on the chest in armadillos, and her litter may contain as many as ten instead of the usual one to four. The small size of the armadillo and its covering of armour enables it to take refuge in the arid scrub of the southern U.S.A., in thorny thickets where larger predators may not be able to penetrate. When caught in open country, its armour is not a complete protection against dogs, coyotes and peccaries, which have learnt to turn it over and attack the soft underparts. But against this is the fact that when alarmed it can make for the thorny scrub, or for its burrow, at a speed often beyond that of dog or man.

Finally, there is an unexpected factor in its behaviour: although heavy for its size—up to seventeen pounds, or nearly a pound for every inch of length—and although burdened with an armour, it can cross streams and rivers. Thus it is able to overcome one of the natural barriers to its spreading. It was at one time thought that the armadillo walked along the bottom to cross a river, but it has since been shown to possess an unusual means of making itself buoyant. When first it enters the water it swims low with the head just above the surface. After a time it becomes more buoyant, having inflated its intestine by taking in air in a series of gasps. Little is known about the exact mechanism of this, but the ability to cross a stretch of water by this method, unusual as it sounds, can be accepted as an observed fact.

At first sight it looks as if an increased abundance of food has caused the resurgence of a species belonging to what, on other counts, appears to be a declining stock. Combined with the natural advantages possessed by the species, its high rate of reproduction, its ability to cross one of the natural bars to increase of range, and also a catholicity of diet, this increased supply of food could be the one more advantageous factor to tip the scale and set the rest in operation. On the other hand, the type of country it has to cross, in parts at least of its range, is arid scrub, and this would seem to rule out increase of food as an operative factor. Nor can we argue that the extension of human settlement has brought about a reduction in its enemies, for the armadillo is much sought after for human consumption, and this would offset any reduction in natural predators. The spread of the armadillo is being closely watched, but it is too early to say whether it is, so to speak, a natural resurgence; that is, one not primarily due to the environment.

One last thing before we leave the armadillos. It is often suggested that the sudden advent of a speedy and nimble-witted predator is the main factor in the extinction of many species. The armadillos of South America do not seem to have suffered much from the intrusion of several carnivores from the north; nor does the presence there of others seem to have affected the recent spread of the nine-banded armadillo to the north. The situation of the sloths is similar: they do not appear to be adversely affected by the invasion of their original homeland by one of the big cats, the jaguar, which is their chief enemy. For, in spite of the general belief to the contrary, it has been shown in the last decade that sloths are by no means rare animals. Those who have made a special study of them in the field report that they are, in fact, very numerous, and that it is their slow-moving habits and the effective camouflage of their alga-infected hair which make them so inconspicuous as to appear rare.

CHAPTER VI

PERIPATUS: WORM-INSECT

THERE is such a diversity of worms and of insects that it would be difficult to pick out one of either class as typical without laying oneself open to severe criticism by the zoological purists. If, for sake of argument, however, we take an earthworm as a typical worm and a beetle as a typical insect, there is a great gulf between them in appearance and in behaviour. So it is difficult to imagine a close relationship between them. If, however, our current views on organic evolution represent an approximation to the truth, then insects have been derived from a worm-like ancestor. Let us consider the similarities between worms and insects. First, there is the ringed or segmented body of the worm, and the obvious segmentation of the beetle's abdomen. In the beetle larva, this segmentation is even more pronounced, of course. In other outward features, on the other hand, worm and beetle appear markedly different. The beetle moves on six legs, the worm on a series of bristles running down either side of the body. The beetle has wings and wing-covers, sensory antennae, obvious and efficient eyes, and a hard armour of chitin clothing the body. The earthworm has none of these things.

Internally, there is a greater similarity between these two invertebrates. Both have the same kind of nervous system. Its main plan comprises two nerve ganglia lying over the front end of the digestive canal, connected by nerve cords running either side round the canal, to connect up below in another pair of ganglia. Thence, it runs back, under the digestive tube to the hind end of the body, and bears at intervals paired ganglia in each segment of the body. In other respects there are also

similarities, as well as differences, but the discussion of them
would lead us into detailed descriptions of comparative
anatomy that would not profit our present theme. It must
suffice to say that in general terms there are sufficient similarities
between an earthworm and an insect to encourage the convinced evolutionist to suspect a common ancestry. At the same
time, there are sufficient differences between them to cause the
sceptic of the theory of evolution to be even more sceptical
of such a common lineage. If, nevertheless, account could be
taken of the structure of all the worms known to science and of
all the insects, as well as of the life-histories of all of them, the
gap would be considerably narrowed. There are, for instance,
among the bristle-worms, the marine relatives of the earthworm,
many with well-developed jaws, many with sensory tentacles
almost worthy of the name of antennae, and some with eyes that
show an approximation to the eyes of the simpler forms of
insects. Yet, to be fair, it would have to be admitted that some
of these similarities could be due to coincidence, or convergence, as we say.

In such a situation the zoologist looks for a "missing link",
which, in practice, is almost the same thing as a living fossil.
In this case one was found as long ago as 1826, in the West
Indies. When first found it was taken to be an unusual kind
of slug. However, its position intermediate between the worms,
on the one hand, and the arthropods, including insects, on the
other, was soon recognised. This animal, which we know as
Peripatus, from a Greek word signifying something that
wanders about, is indeed a living fossil and a missing link as
well.

Peripatus may be briefly described as a lowly terrestrial
arthropod with a caterpillar-like body. It moves about on short
unjointed legs, to the number of nearly a score of pairs, each
leg ending in hook-like claws. The head bears a pair of pointed
antennae and a pair of strong jaws. Breathing is by means of
tracheae. There are some sixty species of peripatus in the damp
forests of the West Indies, Central and South America,

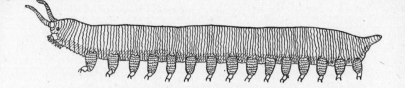

24. PERIPATUS (*Peripatoides novae-zealandiae*) of New
Zealand, one of the several species suggesting a link
between worms and insects.

South Africa, Australia, New Zealand and Malaya. Apart
from its odd appearance resulting from a mixture of worm and
insect characters, and apart from the possibility that it might
prove a link between the worms and the arthropods, peripatus
is highly interesting in its own zoological right. To begin with,
although such a soft-bodied animal would not be expected to
fossilise well, there are remains in the Silurian rocks which
come so close to it that we can say peripatus has persisted
almost unchanged for some 300 million years. This small
degree of change is reflected in the modern species, for although
there are some sixty of these, widely distributed over the southern hemisphere, there is comparatively little difference between
them. There are differences in colour, and in size, the largest
being about four inches long, and in trivial details of structure.
There is even a cave species which, like most cave-dwelling
animals, has lost its colour. Yet, in spite of these differences,
there is still the strongest resemblance between them all.

More remarkable still is the fact, as we shall see when we
come to examine the habits and physiology of peripatus, that
all its species are extremely specialised in the matter of habitat,
and that they are almost as isolated by the conditions of the
habitat as if each were living on an oceanic island. All are
highly susceptible to desiccation, and, taking one thing with
another, it is not easy to see what special qualifications peripatus
possesses to have aided its survival over so long a period. And,
as in all living fossils of great persistence, there is the question

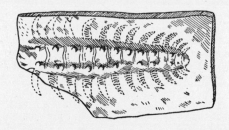

25. A PRE-CAMBRIAN FORERUNNER (*Xenusion*) of
the worm-insect, peripatus.

why they should remain virtually unaltered through all the
climatic and geographical changes. It must cause us seriously
to question whether such changes are indeed the real factors
influencing extinction or survival.

The habitat of peripatus is much the same as that of the more
familiar woodlice—under rotten wood, under stones, or under
the bark of fallen trees. When disturbed its first reaction is often
to eject a milky white fluid, as a jet or a spray, in a single or
double line, to a distance of three to twelve inches. These
sticky threads come from a pair of slime glands, set either side
of the mouth on the underside of the head. The slime itself is
stored in reservoirs on the sides of the body, each like the teat
of the now outmoded fountain-pen filler. The adhesive threads
that solidify from the fluid when it has been ejected can be
drawn out and beaded, like the silk from a spider's spinnerets.
And as with spider's silk, small animals ensnared in it have
little chance of escape. It seems, however, that the threads are
entirely defensive, for although animals so caught may represent
its normal diet, peripatus has not been seen to eat such captives.

Peripatus feeds on various small insects, also termites, woodlice and even large insects, such as grasshoppers, provided
they are recently dead. It may take carrion of a more advanced
kind, however, since in captivity it has been known to take
sheep's liver. There is, moreover, another side to its feeding
which is worthy of at least passing notice. It has been found that

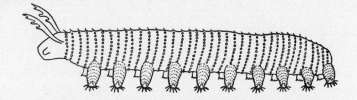

26. ANOTHER SUPPOSED ANCESTOR OF PERIPATUS:
the Cambrian fossil *Ayshesia*.

some peripatus will starve rather than feed in captivity. This is, of course, no new phenomenon. It is common enough in birds, and more especially with mammals that are capable of something approaching emotional behaviour; and it is readily understandable. They have lost their liberty—a valuable possession even to a wild animal. They are being persuaded to take food, not of their own acquiring, and by a strange and frightening being that is, as often as not, foreign to their experience. But we should not have expected peripatus to show a similar reaction, and certainly not for any such reasons as these. Furthermore, we have the curious contrast of an individual reared in captivity, growing and thriving for two years, and then suddenly going on a fatal hunger strike. It is not possible to take these remarks to a more obvious conclusion than this, but they help to underline the suspicion that food is an even more important factor in survival than we normally suppose. There is, moreover, the suggestion in this that the importance of food lies less in the mere presence or absence of nourishing substances, as in a fastidiousness on the part of the animal concerned.

The matter of keeping peripatus in captivity brings us to other aspects of the life and habits of this curious invertebrate. After speaking of a mammal or bird being confronted with its captor, which it can see, we are impelled to wonder about the sense-organs of peripatus. The quasi slug-like nature of the creature and its slug-like tentacles almost suggest that we shall find the eyes, like those of a slug, on the ends of those tentacles. They are, in fact, at the base of each antenna. These eyes have, however, very limited powers. They are probably incapable of recording more than variations in the brightness of light and are unable to see forwards, only upwards. Apart from the antennae and the eyes, the main sense organs are the numerous hairs clothing most of the body, functioning probably as organs of touch, taste and perhaps smell. Peripatus is, however, peculiarly sensitive to the state of dampness or dryness of its surroundings. Dr. S. M. Manton, who has made a special study of peripatus tells us that: "In an ordinarily dry room it will lose a third of its body weight in less than four hours." In other words, it will dry up twice as quickly as an earthworm, and "forty times as rapidly as a smooth skinned caterpillar of the same size".

This susceptibility to desiccation involves an evolutionary paradox. The earthworm, lower in the animal scale, has a wet skin permeable to water and also more readily allowing the passage of water outwards. Although usually spoken of as a terrestrial animal, it is closely linked with damp or wet soil, and needs, in fact, a semi aquatic habitat. Peripatus has progressed further towards the ideal for a terrestrial life in so far as it has acquired a dry skin, being in this respect much nearer to the typical insect. On the other hand, its mode of breathing is by tracheae; that is, by tubes which conduct air from openings— the spiracles—on the surface of the body, to the inner tissues. This is in line with what has happened in insects; but whereas the tracheae of insects are much branched, requiring fewer spiracles to supply the body with air, and whereas the spiracles themselves are capable of being closed, the tracheae of peripatus are simple tubes, the spiracles are numerous and there is no mechanism for closing them. In a dry atmosphere, therefore, there is a heavy loss of water through the peripatus respiratory system. In other words, it has progressed sufficiently far to have lost the advantages possessed by the earthworm without having acquired the more efficient structures developed in insects.

The susceptibility to desiccation results in another bar to progress. A colony of peripatus in one locality will be isolated from the next colony if the intervening terrain is dry. Although widely distributed, therefore, its occurrence is local, and the several genera collectively known as peripatus comprise a number of localised species, differing only slightly between themselves. This looks as if the all-important mixing of the gene material necessary to the evolution of new types has little chance to be effected.

Although in its bodily characters, peripatus is primitive, marked specialisation has occurred in other directions. The sexes are separate and breeding is by a simple form of coupling, the male depositing spermatozoa in a capsule on the body of the female. Beneath the capsule, white blood corpuscles in the female's body invade and break through the skin, and, as the lower wall of the capsule ruptures, the spermatozoa are released into the female bloodstream. Through it, they find their way to the ovaries and fertilise the eggs. The fertilisation is not a simple process, however, for in a female just sexually mature the young egg-cells use the sperms as food and, with this only as nourishment, grow for a year before they are ready for fertilisation. Then, at the next coupling, they are fertilised, and the superfluous sperms go to feed the next generation of egg-cells. There is a further overlap in many species in that, although young are born every year, the period of pregnancy is thirteen months, so that for one month in every year the mature female carries two sets of embryos, one in the early stages of development and the other near the end of their development.

In most species of peripatus the young are born alive. One Australian species lays eggs with a large yolk, but in most others the embryos are nourished through the uterine wall, and in one South American species there is a placenta very like that of the mammals. Taking the genus as a whole, therefore, there is a remarkable mixture of primitive with highly specialised characters, and it is not inconceivable that these specialised features, especially those concerned with reproduction, have had a considerable influence on the continued survival. Before speculating further, however, it is worth while turning to such fossil evidence as we have.

The "living fossil" fish, the Coelacanth, caused a stir largely for this reason, that the coelacanths had long been known from their fossil remains. These were widespread, and between the age when coelacanths were numerous and the discovery of the single living specimen there was a long interval of time. In the case of peripatus, or rather, of the class Prototracheata to which it belongs, the position is exactly reversed. The living peripatus has long been known to the zoologists. The living animals are numerous but confined to widely separated regions, and between the present age when Prototracheata are not uncommon in certain localities and the rocks in which a very few fossil remains have been found there is a long interval of time. We might almost call peripatus a case of an inverted living fossil, for there is no evidence that Prototracheata were formerly abundant and that the animals living today have survived beyond their epoch. There is no tangible evidence, in other words, that the present day is not the Age of Proto-tracheata. Indeed, if we had to rely on the evidence of our senses of sight and touch, we could draw no other conclusion. Nor need such a conclusion be necessarily remarkable. It would be possible to draw an analogy with the barnacles. Their remains are numerous in the rocks from the Mesozoic onwards (the earlier barnacle-like fossils occurring in the Paleozoic are now alleged to be not barnacles at all). Yet, T. H. Withers, the leading authority on these animals, has said: "The present-day may be truly regarded as the Age of Cirri-pedes (i.e. Barnacles)." There is, as I have said, no tangible evidence that this is not the case with peripatus.

It would be possible to pursue another line of argument in favour of this view. Thus, it is axiomatic that organic evolution is not necessarily a progression from the simple to the compli-cated, or specialised. There is often the reverse, the evolution of a simple organ or organism from a previously complicated or

specialised organism, a process known as secondary simplification. In peripatus, as we have seen, the bodily characters
are simple, and therefore usually called primitive, yet the
development is advanced, or specialised, even to the point of
one species showing a placental development of the embryo
comparable to the highest attainment in the most highly
evolved animals, the mammals.

If the zoologist, in the complete absence of palaeontological
knowledge, were to try to visualise an animal that was intermediate between the typical worm and the typical insect, he
could hardly escape reconstructing, as his hypothetical missing
link, an animal closely resembling peripatus in gross structure.
If, now, this same zoologist were to enlist the collaboration of
the palaeontologist to forecast when such an animal should be
found in the geological succession their joint arguments would
follow some such lines as these. There are a few obscure fossils
in the later Pre-Cambrian rocks which resemble traces of
worms. Then, in the next succeeding period, the Cambrian,
the rocks are filled with the remains of undoubted arthropods,
the Trilobites. These continue to be abundant in the next
period, the Ordovician, while in the ensuing period, the
Silurian, we have the earliest remains of an alleged insect, mere
wing traces, and by the Devonian period there are arthropods
in plenty: millipedes, mites, spiders, crustacea and wingless
insects. If, indeed, the Prototracheata do represent something
close to the ancestral stock of all arthropods, including insects,
then we should expect to find the earliest remains in the
Cambrian at least, and probably also in the later Pre-Cambrian.
Moreover, if our ideas about the genesis of land faunas from
marine animals is correct, we should expect to find that the Pre-
Cambrian and Cambrian Prototracheata were marine. And
this is precisely what has been found. The circumstantial evidence is, therefore, strongly in favour of regarding peripatus as
an archaic survival and not as an animal secondarily simplified
which has come, by convergence, to resemble an ancient
type.

8

There are only two undoubted fossil Prototracheata. The earliest is that known as *Xenusion*, an impression of about a half or two-thirds of an animal, in a block of Pre-Cambrian limestone derived from Sweden. The total length of this impression is some four inches with a diameter of an inch at the widest part of the body. The impression, although imperfect, recalls strongly the general appearance of the living Prototracheata, and although there are differences in the pattern on the surface of the body, the numerous pairs of legs are strongly reminiscent of the short baggy legs of the living animal. The second fossil, *Ayshesia*, of the Cambrian, is even more like the modern peripatus in general appearance, and although nothing can be known about its internal structure or its development, it can be fairly safely assumed that both were simple and that the main line of advance was in these and not in the outward form. While it cannot yet be proved beyond a doubt that peripatus is the lineal descendant of *Ayshesia*, all reasonable deductions point in that direction, and render it a reasonable assumption that of all living fossils peripatus holds pride of place, having undergone remarkably little change over a period of 500 million years (*see* fig. 51 on page 132).

A brief digression may be made here to consider the history of some forms related to peripatus. The phylum Arthropoda, of which the Prototracheata form a class, includes also the Trilobita, now wholly extinct, and four groups abundantly represented at the present time. The first of these are the Myriapoda, comprising the millipedes and centipedes. Then come the Crustacea, familiar to us in the form of the crabs, shrimps, lobsters, woodlice, water fleas and so on; the Insecta, needing no introduction, and the Arachnida, including spiders, mites, scorpions; and, last of all, king-crabs. These last three will be dealt with in greater detail in later chapters; for the moment we shall concern ourselves with the millipedes and centipedes.

The first satisfactory evidence of life on land is found in the Silurian (320 to 350 million years ago), and consists of the

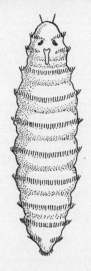

27. A PRIMITIVE WORM (*Dinophilus*) LIVING TODAY,
its body composed of few segments.

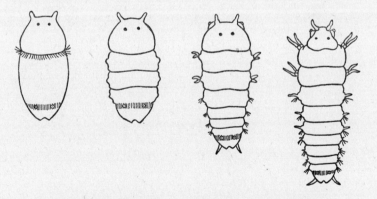

28. DEVELOPMENT OF A MARINE BRISTLE-WORM
from the larva (left), to show the general resemblance
to early arthropods.

remains of millipedes and insects. Thereafter, their remains
testify to the persistence, in very much the original form, of both
these animals. These remains are, however, much more
abundant than those of the Prototracheata, which, as we have
seen, are represented by two fossils only, while at the present
time both millipedes and centipedes are represented by thousands of species distributed throughout the world, in practically
every kind of terrestrial habitat. Their long persistence and the
relatively small amount of change they have undergone are
more remarkable than in the Prototracheata, but they do not
qualify for the inclusion in the vague category of living fossils
because they are still so abundant today. Even so, they offer
yet another type bridging the gulf between the annelid worms
and the higher arthropods, such as the insects and spiders.

Millipedes and centipedes are worm-like, with elongated
cylindrical bodies, somewhat flattened from above downwards
in centipedes. The body, like that of the typical worm, consists
of a number of segments, all alike except for a few at the front
end of the body. Each segment bears legs, a pair to each
segment in the centipedes and two pairs to each segment in the
millipedes. The legs are composed of a number of joints and
are not so clearly differentiated or highly organised as those of
insects, spiders and crustacea. To that extent they may be
termed primitive. The head comprises several segments fused
to form a region distinct from, and perceptibly unlike, the
parts or segments forming the rest of the body. This is a feature
also of the higher arthropods, but there is the difference that in
them the segments of the rest of the body have undergone
change and often fusion. In the gross architecture of the body,
therefore, the Myriapoda are halfway towards that of their more
advanced relatives.

Breathing, in the Myriapoda, is by tracheae; these open on to
the exterior through paired slits, or stigmata, on almost every
segment, but in so far as the openings are numerous, the
breathing apparatus of millipedes and centipedes approaches
that of peripatus, while in the structure of the tracheae there is

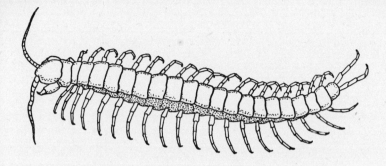

29. LARGE CENTIPEDE (*Scolopendra subspinipes*) common throughout the tropics. The last segment carries a pair of legs. (Compare with fig. 30.)

an approach to the insects. There is the usual ventral nerve cord, which is primitive in that it stretches practically from one end of the body to the other with a pair of nerve-knots in each segment. The digestive tube is simple, yet foreshadows some of the more specialised organs found in the insects. The blood vascular system includes a many chambered heart, lying above the digestive tube, and extending almost from one end of the body to the other. In this, again, there is a similarity with the same system in insects but it is more primitive in design. From these and other intermediate characters, it is reasonable to describe the millipedes and centipedes as links between the more primitive Prototracheata and the more specialised insects.

Since the Prototracheata and the Myriapoda represent very close and almost successive stages in the evolution of the arthropods, and since their history can, in both cases, be traced back to the earliest fossil-bearing rocks, it is a natural question to ask why the one should be now so widespread and the other restricted to a few localities. The first thing to be noticed is that the present-day representatives of the Prototracheata, the various species of peripatus, are all found in the warmer climates, although in Tasmania they may be under snow, on the mountains, for part of the year. Within that zone of the earth's surface they are restricted and localised to damp habitats, indeed are highly intolerant of drying influences. The Myriapods on the other hand, and certainly the centipedes, seem to be indifferent to changes in temperature, and there is no reason to suppose that they are any more susceptible to changes in humidity. In fact, the secret of their success may be this independence of a moist habitat. As to this last, they are found in hot and cold countries, in barren regions or in fertile districts. The classic example of their wide tolerance of temperature ranges is Sinclair's observation that two species of centipede abundant on the hot luxuriant plains of Cyprus are common and still very active on the snow of the neighbouring Mount Troodos. Another point to be noted is that some species of Myriapoda are found between tide-marks and can withstand long periods of immersion in sea-water.

Centipedes are carnivorous, their food being insects and their larvae, worms and other small invertebrates. They are active, able both to kill their prey and also to defend themselves with poison fangs, and show some degree of maternal care of the young, or rather of the eggs. As the eggs are laid they are coated with a sticky fluid from glands in the body of the female, who then rolls each egg over and over until it is covered with particles of earth. Effectively camouflaged, the egg stands little chance of destruction by predators, and the young hatching out are already in possession of functional poison fangs. Millipedes are by contrast herbivorous, slow-moving, and depend for defence on stink glands which emit an unpleasant odour and a fluid containing prussic acid. Maternal care is even more advanced. The female, using a sticky fluid from her salivary glands mixed with particles of earth, constructs a rounded nest with a hole in the top. Into this she lays up to a hundred eggs, then plugs the entrance with her own make of cement.

Apart from other considerations, millipedes and centipedes have obvious advantages helping towards survival. Their food

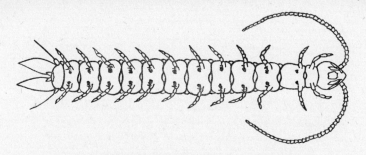

30. ONE OF THE SYMPHYLA, a group of arthropods looking very like centipedes but distinguished among other things by the two cerci on the last segment.

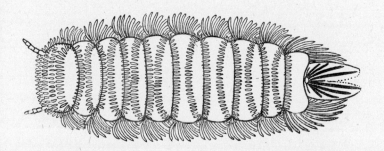

31. A PRIMITIVE MILLIPEDE (*Polyxenus lagurus*) living under stones or bark, its body covered with scale-like hairs.

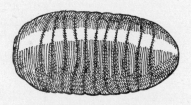

32. A MILLIPEDE FROM BORNEO (*Zephronia impressa*), its body composed of 11 to 13 segments only.

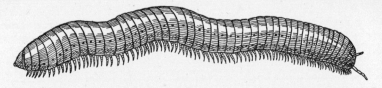

33. A MILLIPEDE FROM THE PHILIPPINES (*Spirobolus
cupulifer*): tropical millipedes may be up to 10 inches
in length.

is abundant, they have an effective means of defence, and there
is a degree of maternal care of the young. Despite the great
differences in other respects, all species of peripatus also possess
two of these attributes: the unpleasant secretion ejected when
disturbed, and an abundance of food. This last can also be
bracketed with the habitat: since the animal lives under rotten
wood or stones, it is not likely to be short of those materials
which form its favourite habitat. And since its food comprises
a wide range of small invertebrates, this same habitat ensures an
abundance of nourishment.

It would be unwise, and probably unprofitable, at this
juncture, to speculate further on the causes of survival in
peripatus or the Myriapoda. Two comments are, however,
permissible. The first is, that from the little we can glean in both
cases, it seems to be implied that no one single factor, but
rather a concatenation of factors is responsible for survival.
The second is rather a satirical comment: that the concept of
living fossil—or, for that matter of missing link—arises not so
much on scientific grounds as from human psychology. Man is
fascinated by rarities, and animals that are rare, relatively rare,
or on the verge of extinction, appeal to him as much as a
unique archaeological treasure or any other rarity. Zoological
rarities have, of course, a scientific value as does also the
archaeological rarity, but the prominence accorded them,
especially in the popular literature, is out of proportion to the
contribution they make to our final understanding of the living
world. Only this can account for the fact that in a popular book

on natural history, often the text-book of zoology also, several pages will be devoted to peripatus and the whole of the Myria-poda are dismissed in a paragraph or two. Yet both are living witnesses from the remote past, descendants of a stock that has survived almost unchanged for over 500 million years.

CHAPTER VII

KING-CRABS AND THEIR RELATIVES

THE name Arthropoda is derived from two Greek words and means literally jointed foot, but with the inconsistency that characterises the greater part of scientific nomenclature it is applied to animals having jointed legs. A further inconsistency follows from the fact that it is scarcely ever possible to pigeonhole living organisms neatly; on every other count it is necessary to include the Prototracheata (peripatus) in this group, although the legs are not jointed in the usual sense. This is necessary because they resemble, in so many other respects, the typical arthropods, such as crustacea, insects, spiders, millipedes, centipedes and the rest.

The relationships of the various classes of Arthropoda and their probable lines of evolution can be expressed diagrammatically (*see* fig. 51). According to this, from an original Pre-Cambrian stock arose the Prototracheata, now represented by those genera known collectively as peripatus; and later, in the Cambrian, came the Trilobita, of which over a thousand species are known from the rocks of that period. These represent about half the Arthropoda living at that time. The rest include certain shrimp-like Crustacea, including those belonging to the genus *Waptia*, of which more will be said later.

We speak of a main arthropod stock, but such a thing is purely hypothetical. It is a vague concept such as each of us has when referring to our ancestors of the last few centuries. It is a shadowy visualisation of a sequence of generations, each having its peculiarities, its own way of life, yet each merging imperceptibly into the other and forming as a whole a succession

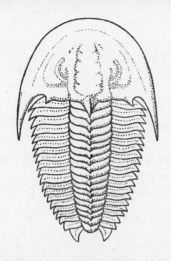

34. TRILOBITES FROM THE EARLIEST CAMBRIAN ROCKS. Trilobites have been extinct two hundred million years.

which cannot be denied, even if it cannot be proved. We believe in the reality of the stock from which we have sprung largely from the logic of the situation and the relics each of the later generations has left. In dealing with the succession of animal life the relics are often fewer than with human ancestors. Yet, just as one human family may have the house filled with heirlooms, such as portraits and the like, from many genera-tions back, and another family has nothing but the occasional relic from the preceding generation, so some groups of animals are represented by abundant fossils from almost every period of the past, while others can be linked with the past mainly by what can be deduced from the present, together with analogies drawn with other groups better represented.

Even as the main stock is a vague hypothetical conception, so are many of its offshoots also. We have, therefore, to content ourselves with saying that at a subsequent period, soon after the Trilobita arose, the Eurypterida, the so-called sea-scorpions, as well as the Arachnida (spiders, mites and ticks) and, slightly later, the Myriapoda (centipedes and millipedes) come into view. We can suggest, with a fair degree of confidence, that ancestral arthropods, forsaking an aquatic life for one on land, probably gave rise to these last two groups and also to the insects.

A simple summary of this kind may make it appear that too much is being taken for granted. Brief descriptions of the various groups will do something to offset this. The Proto-tracheata, and especially peripatus, have received full attention in a previous chapter. The next class in order of time, the Trilobita, comprises numerous species of marine arthropods which reached their maximum development during the Cambrian and Ordovician periods and became extinct in the Permian. Trilobites are so-called from the tri-lobed appearance of the back. The segments of the body on the dorsal surface are each divided into three parts, the whole producing a median lobe, or axis, flanked by two lateral lobes, or pleura. The general run of trilobites were mainly an inch or two long, but some species reached over two feet in length. In all of them the body was generally a flattened oval, and besides the three lobes already mentioned, it was divided transversely into three regions: a head, thorax and abdomen. The head was covered by a continuous shield; the thorax was composed of a variable number of free segments; and the abdomen consisted of a number of segments more or less completely fused. The legs were delicate and are rarely preserved. Where these have been found they have proved to be forked in the outer half, and those of the thorax are found to carry gills. The head carried a pair of antennae and four pairs of other appendages. Many trilobites were capable of rolling into a ball, in the manner of some woodlice.

The Eurypterida comprise a class of aquatic arthropods, the remains of which are found in all Paleozoic rocks after the Cambrian and which became extinct with the end of the Permian. They are usually assumed to be related to the scor-pions and spiders, but more closely to the king-crabs, with

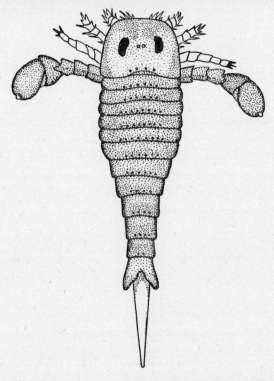

35. REMARKABLE   PRESERVATION   OF   SEA-
SCORPION. Extinct three hundred million years, the
outer coat of *Eurypterus fischeri* is still perfectly preserved.

which they are often associated in a separate class, the Merostomata. The Eurypterida had a cephalothorax bearing six pairs
of legs, the last pair being usually paddle-like. The abdomen
was tapering and consisted of thirteen segments. The largest
Eurypterida were more than six feet long, the largest arthropods
of all time. One species deserves special mention. Its remains
are found in the Upper Silurian limestone of the Island of
Oesel, in the Baltic. This is *Eurypterus fischeri*, five inches long.
The chitinous covering to the body in the Oesel fossils is
so perfectly preserved that it is unchanged in its chemical
or physical composition. The rock in which the fossils are

contained can, therefore, be dissolved, leaving the outer casing of the eurypterids in as good condition as when the soft parts had first decayed away, 320 million years ago. The result is that these fossils are better known than those of any other extinct arthropod.

The class Arachnida includes spiders, scorpions, harvesters, mites and ticks, with several less familiar groups, all having the eyes simple and the body divided into two parts, a cephalo-thorax and an abdomen. Locomotion is by four pairs of legs. Breathing is usually by lung books, but some arachnids have tracheae although these are different from the comparable organs in insects. The great majority of Arachnida are terres-trial. The young are generally hatched from eggs, growth being by periodical moults, the development being direct except in mites that have a larval stage bearing three pairs of legs only. Although numerous fossils are known they are mainly from the Paleozoic, the Mesozoic Arachnida being relatively poorly represented. Scorpions are probably the best represented, being found from the Silurian onwards. Spiders and mites do not appear until the next period, the Devonian; and harvesters in the Carboniferous. There are, in addition, as in the other classes of arthropods, orders which flourished at some time in the Paleozoic but became extinct towards its close or soon after. The first fossil scorpions are remarkably like the present-day ones. But for their prevalence in modern times, and the archaic nature of the group Arachnida generally, there would be much to be said for regarding present-day scorpions as living fossils. The same is true of mites, which today inhabit the earth in vast numbers of both populations and species, and which have come down relatively unchanged from the time of the Rhynie Chert of the Devonian.

Incidentally, the Rhynie Chert was originally a peat with plants growing in it, which is now preserved in solid blocks of stone. The assumption is that the peat was rapidly petrified by water containing flinty matter in solution, probably from hot springs. The plants are preserved growing erect, as they grew

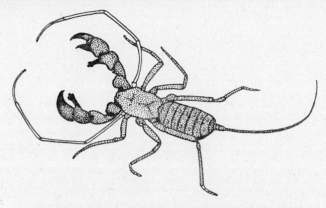

36. WHIP-SCORPIONS LIVE UNDER STONES AND BARK: now found in warmer parts of America and south-east Asia, they have persisted since the Carboniferous.

in the open-air of Devonian times. The small invertebrates, insects, woodlice and mites are preserved *in situ* in the peat.

The typical arthropod has a segmented body, but most of the Arachnida are unsegmented. In the early spiders, however, as late as the Carboniferous period, the body was clearly seg-mented, with the abdomen containing twelve segments. This condition is still preserved in some present-day arachnids. In the so-called primitive spiders of the sub-order Liphistio-morphae, found today in small numbers in India, Malaysia and Japan, the abdomen comprises twelve segments. This, as we shall see, is a feature of archaic insects. The false-scorpions, the largest of which is no more than a quarter of an inch long and the smallest very much less than this, look like a cross between a scorpion and a spider. They are common throughout the world in the warmer countries. In them, also, the abdomen is made up of twelve segments, and the thorax is segmented, consisting of three distinct segments. So, although the typical spiders of today look so unlike the typical insects now living, there is much to suggest a close relationship between their ancestors of Paleozoic times.

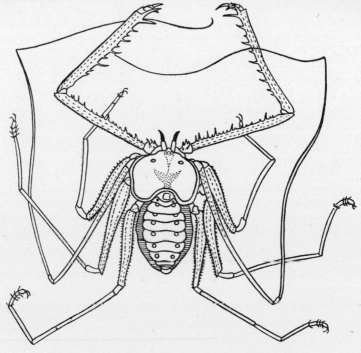

37. A RELATIVE OF WHIP-SCORPIONS, *Damon johnstoni* also survives from the Carboniferous.

In the primitive spiders, book-scorpions and false-scorpions, we have a similar situation to that found in scorpions: their claims to being recognised as living fossils are strong. It is probably because they are small and of inconspicuous habit that nothing dramatic has ever been associated with them. So they are not normally spoken of as living fossils.

Most people have a general idea of what is meant by a crustacean; crabs, lobsters, shrimps and prawns are sufficiently well known, even if water-fleas, brine shrimps, and others that make up this diversified class, are not so familiar. Since, moreover, particular attention will be given in a subsequent chapter to certain supposedly archaic crustacea that have some claim to being considered living fossils, a scanty summary of the class

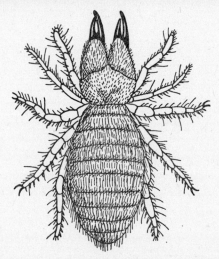

38. A PRIMITIVE RELATIVE OF SPIDERS, *Hexisopus*
looks like a living fossil but no fossils of it are known.

as a whole will suffice here. The body is usually covered with a
chitinous outer layer, and in the larger crustacea this is hardened
with calcareous matter to form a firm shell. The head and thorax
are usually united into a cephalothorax, the abdominal segments remaining mobile. In the higher crustacea the number of
segments is twenty to twenty-one, but in the lower forms it is
much more variable. There are usually two pairs of antennae
and the numerous limbs are differentiated into mouth-parts,
pincers, swimming legs and walking legs. Certain bivalve
crustaceans, termed Ostracods, are known from the Cambrian, and some shrimp-like forms are found in the Silurian
rocks.

The last class of Arthropoda to be considered are the Myriapoda,* the centipedes and millipedes. Centipedes are elongated
and somewhat flattened, with the body divided into numerous
segments each bearing a pair of legs. They are predaceous on

* Myriapoda is used here as a convenient inclusive term. The practice today
is to recognise four classes: Diplopoda (millipedes), Chilopoda (centipedes),
Symphyla and Pauropoda.

9

insects and other small invertebrates, the front pair of legs being modified into poison fangs. Although usually small, some tropical species measure up to a foot long. The slowly moving millipedes are herbivorous. The body is more cylindrical than that of the centipedes, and each segment, apart from the first three in the front of the body, bears a pair of legs on each side. The first millipedes are known from the Devonian, the first centipedes are from the Upper Carboniferous.

These few pages devoted to characters of the Arthropoda are intended merely to outline a picture of the affinities of these various groups of jointed-legged animals that take us back to the early pages of fossil history. Within this picture we see groups arising in the earliest periods of the fossil record and dying out before the beginning of the Mesozoic. There are others, like the spiders, which arose somewhat later in the Paleozoic, and which have undergone, for the most part, perceptible changes during the span of 300 million years or more. Alongside them, however, are certain smaller groups: for example, the false-scorpions, including the book-scorpions and whip-tailed scorpions, which in spite of having undergone changes still retain many archaic characters. Finally, there are the centipedes and the millipedes, that, like the scorpions, have shown relatively little change throughout their long history.

There are two further points that emerge. The first takes us back to the rocket simile. In an earlier chapter this was used in an over-simplified form. To give a representation that is nearer the truth we have to suppose the successive showers of sparks to be far less uniform than in any pyrotechnic display. To represent the arthropods, some explosions would need to give rise to many sparks of long duration (representing the centipedes and millipedes), some to many sparks of short duration (the trilobites), others with a few sparks of long duration (the scorpions), a few sparks of short duration (the eurypterids); and, finally, we have to imagine some of the main showers crackling and popping, sending out a miscellaneous assortment of subsidiary showers (the spiders, the insects and the

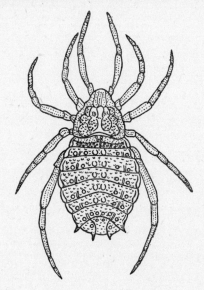

39. FOSSIL HARVEST-SPIDER found in a nodule from
a coal-mine.

crustacea). And with them all are the solitary sparks, falling
out of dying showers and continuing their solitary path earth-
wards (the more typical living fossils). This brings us to the
second point, that a horizontal line drawn across such a display
at any given time would transect groups of like sparks, some
large and some small, as well as the solitary sparks. In other
words, every geological horizon can have its living fossil, the
form that has persisted from a group that had at that time
otherwise become extinct.

The question naturally arises, how far we are justified in
assuming that all the animals included in the Arthropoda have
a common starting point. Let us suppose there were no such
things as fossils, or that none had been found or studied. The
zoologist, the student of living animals, would suspect affinities
between them. He would find on dissecting, say, a spider, a
beetle, a scorpion, a centipede, a lobster and so on, that the
internal structure of each bore a strong resemblance to that of

the others. There would be the same ventral nerve-cord, with a similar arrangement in all species of the nerve-ganglia. The structure of the digestive system would be similar, and the arrangement of the blood-vessels would not be so different that homologies, that is, structures having the same origin, even although they may differ markedly in the adult, could not be made out. Externally, there would be the same chitinous exoskeleton, the jointed legs, similar sense-organs, the segmentation of the body with the tendency to fusion in the first five segments to form a discrete head, and the tendency in subsequent segments to form a recognisable thorax. There would be, further, the marked tendency in so many groups for the head and thorax to fuse to form a cephalothorax.

In living organisms, moreover, it is possible to follow the course of development, step by step, and to recognise relationships not always visible in the adult. For example, barnacles that were once thought to be molluscs proved to be related to crabs and lobsters, once the larval stages were known and found to be closely similar to those of the more typical crustacea. Even the development of particular organs in the larva of one species may help to elucidate structures, otherwise puzzling, in the adult of some other species of arthropod. So, by the examination of tissues and organs, of similarities in physiology, life histories, even habits and behaviour, a vast jig-saw can be pieced together. In it, all living species could be spread out, revealing intermediates connecting one outstanding type with another and suggesting possible lines of evolution within the group. Let us repeat, all this could be done with living species alone. Even so, there would be gaps in the knowledge, which could be bridged in imagination but not in actuality.

When the palaeontologist, the student of the remains of animals long since dead, brings his evidence to the jig-saw, he is able to fill in many of these gaps. What is, perhaps, even more important, he is able to show, usually, that the lines of thought and the conclusions of the zoologist are very near to those resulting from his own studies. In other instances, he is

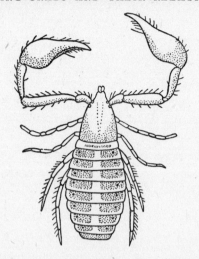

40. FALSE-SCORPIONS LIVE UNDER BARK and in old books.

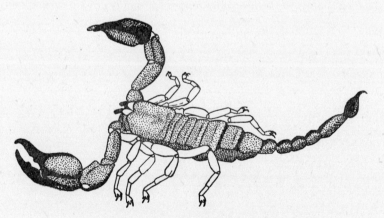

41. SCORPIONS FEED ON INSECTS and live under stones, logs or bark of fallen trees.

able to bring fresh light to bear on problems that have, perhaps, baffled the zoologist. Palaeontology and Zoology are sciences that differ in the materials studied. The palaeontologist deals with animals* long since dead, and mainly with their hard parts, and all too often with fragments only of these; but to compensate for this he has the added dimension of time. The zoologist deals essentially with the whole organism, but without historical perspective. Thus, the two are complementary and mutually interdependent, in that the findings of the one may assist or corroborate the findings of the other. And one of the more powerful links between the two studies is provided by the living fossils. For example, the presence of the foramen or opening in the top of the skull, so marked a feature of extinct reptiles and amphibia, might have been impossible to interpret, if fossils alone had been studied. The invariable presence of the pineal body in the vertebrate brain may have provided a basis for inspired guesswork on the purpose of the foramen. The presence of the paired body, with one member of it so obviously an eye, in tuatara and certain lizards, puts the matter beyond the realm of supposition.

Attention has been drawn, earlier in this chapter, to our broad picture of the geological history of the Arthropoda, with especial reference to the history of the spiders and their rela-tives. We have seen, for example, how the various classes are related in time and how the structure of one group reveals affinities with another group. We have seen the segmented scorpions persisting with little change from the Silurian to the present day, and the spiders starting in the Devonian with segmented bodies, and losing that segmentation in the course of changes down to the present time. It is not possible here to go more fully into the details, and attention must now be trans-ferred to a relative of the scorpions and spiders, the king-crab.

One of the first records of the king-crab, or horseshoe-crab, is in *Historia Animalium*, by Joannes Jonstonius, published in

---

* The sister science, Botany, is not forgotten, and there is the science of Palaeobotany, of which the same thing may be said as of Zoology.

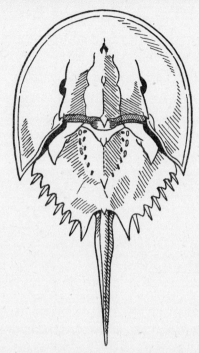

42. THE FIRST LIVING FOSSIL TO ATTRACT ATTEN-
TION. The king-crab appears in the natural history
books of the sixteenth century.

1558. Opposite page 24 is plate VII showing views of
both upper and under surfaces, remarkably accurate in detail
by comparison with other illustrations in that work. Jonstonius
makes no reference to the drawing in his text, but the picture
is labelled *Cancer mollucensis*, that is, the crab from the Moluccas.
For a long time this crab and other king-crabs since discovered
were included in the Crustacea. Since then their affinities have
been continually in doubt. Ray Lankester classified them with
the Arachnida. Other authorities have placed them, together
with the Eurypterida, in a separate class, the Merostomata, but
this has been disputed by yet other authorities, who place them
in a class of their own, the Xiphosura, separating them even
from the Eurypterida.

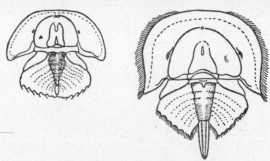

43. LARVAE OF THE KING-CRAB: two stages in their development showing superficial likeness to the extinct trilobites.

This difference of opinion on how the king-crab should be classified is alone an indication of its unusual characteristics. Two of these call for special mention: it has persisted practically unchanged since Devonian times, that is, for 300 million years; and its larvae resemble superficially the trilobites that flourished at that time and became extinct by the end of the Paleozoic period. Further, there have been found, in the Cambrian, forms known respectively as *Synxyphosura* and *Limulava* which are regarded by some workers as close relatives of the king-crab.

As often as not the king-crab is referred to by a generic name *Limulus*. Moreover, there is a tendency to speak of *the* king-crab or of *Limulus* as if there were only one species now; or, indeed, as if this one species had come down unchanged over the last 300 million years. In fact, at the present day, five species can be recognised, distributed between three distinct genera. This is worthy of emphasis, for when it is said that a particular animal has survived unchanged—or even if we are more cautious and say it has survived relatively unchanged—that does not mean that the same species is living today as was alive 300 million years ago, or whatever the time span may be. Since the earliest known king-crab remains in the Devonian, there have been continual changes, producing at each stage new

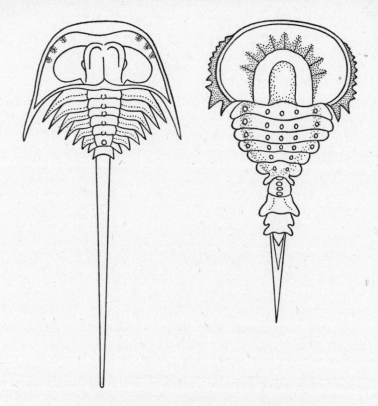

44. CLOSE RELATIVES OF THE KING-CRABS which
died out many millions of years ago.

genera and new species. There have, however, been no abrupt
changes and at all times the animal or its remains can be
recognised beyond a doubt as the one we call the king-crab.

The five species living today are as follows: *Limulus poly-
phemus*, living off the eastern coast of North America, from the
coast of Maine to Yucatan; *Carcinoscorpius rotundicauda*, from
the south of Japan; and three species of *Tachypleus*, *T. gigas*
from Malaysia, *T. hoeveni* from the Moluccas, and *T. tridentatus*
ranging from North Borneo to the seas off China and southern
Japan. In its discontinuous distribution, therefore, the king-crab

conforms to the pattern of one type of living fossil, that in which a few widely distributed species have survived.

Horseshoe-crab is more nearly descriptive of this ancient survivor than king-crab, for there is little majestic about it except its slow and seemingly dignified gait, and the largest, living off the coast of North America, does not exceed two feet in length. In justification of the alternative common name, the cephalothorax is horseshoe-shaped, or crescentic, in outline, and the small abdomen, in which the segments are fused to form a single piece, is hinged to the hinder edge of this unusually large carapace. From the hind end of the abdomen a long sword-shaped tail extends backward. At about the middle of the upper surface of the carapace are two large compound eyes and a median pair of simple eyes. On the under surface, six pairs of legs arise from the region of a small centrally placed mouth, and on the abdomen are small swimming legs, each with a leaf-shaped book-gill attached.

King-crabs live in the shallower waters, where they dig into the sand or mud for worms and molluscs. The female lays two to three hundred eggs, which she buries deep in the sand in the intertidal zone, migrating in from the offshore waters to do so. Three weeks later the "trilobite" larvae emerge, being sustained by the yolk in the egg-sac for the first month of larval life, after which they assume the appearance of the adult in miniature.

It is a sad commentary, which we may give incidentally, that today, off the coast of the U.S.A., this strange animal which caught the attention of the natural historian Joannes Jonstonius four centuries ago, which has been the subject of several erudite monographs, and which has left the zoological world guessing as to its true position in the animal kingdom, is caught by the hundred on its inshore migrations, including its spawning migrations. Its eggs are used for pig and poultry food, and the adults are crushed and used as ground fertiliser. Another unfortunate circumstance is that the method used in trapping takes young and old alike.

CHAPTER VIII

SHRIMPS IN ODD CORNERS

T HE Crustacea have been aptly called the Insects of the Sea; and, although they do not compare with insects in numbers of species their populations are probably comparable. From the drift-line, under the rotting seaweed just above high-tide mark, through the shore pools to the ocean abysses they are present everywhere, often in countless numbers, especially in the surface waters where they form a large part of the plankton. In the fresh waters they are present, in the form of water fleas at least, in every pond, lake, stream and river. Some have taken to the land, like the woodlice of the garden, wood and field, or like the land crabs of the tropics. Ranging in size from the microscopic to the giant crabs and lobsters, they present an apparently endless diversity of shape. Yet, if we exclude the barnacles and certain crustacea that have become parasitic, that endless diversity is seen more as variations on a basic design.

The history of the Crustacea takes us back to the Cambrian period, to the shrimp-like *Waptia*, nearly two inches long. But although poorly represented in that period, in the Ordovician another form of crustacean, the ostracod, swarmed in the shallow seas. In the next period, the Silurian, the ostracods, still common, include forms like *Leperditia*, an inch long, together with another shrimp-like crustacean, the *Ceratiocaris*. By the Devonian, crustacea had appeared on land, for in the Rhynie Chert forms resembling woodlice are to be found. It is not until the Triassic, nearly 100 million years later, that we have the first fossils of the larger crustacea, which are lobster-like. In the Jurassic these become more numerous, and

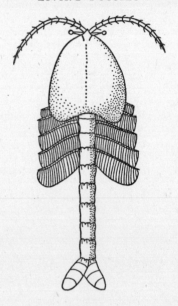

45. AN EXTINCT SHRIMP-LIKE CRUSTACEAN:
Waptia, from the Cambrian of Canada, with leaf-
shaped swimming limbs.

the first crabs are found. Through the Cretaceous the lobsters
remain predominant, but in the Eocene, beginning 75 million
years ago, crabs begin to overshadow them. By the Pliocene,
which began 15 million years ago, the crustacean faunas of the
seas were very like those of today, although many of the species
and some of the genera have since become extinct. Finally, in
the Pleistocene, a crustacean fauna had come into existence
which was very like that today, except that some of its members
had a different distribution.

There is a particular interest attaching to this geological
succession for it agrees with the sequence of classification arrived
at on studying the structure of the living crustacea. Thus,
the class Crustacea is subdivided into five sub-classes: the
Branchiopoda, the Ostracoda, the Copepoda, the Cirripedia
and the Malacostraca. If we exclude the Cirripedia (barnacles)

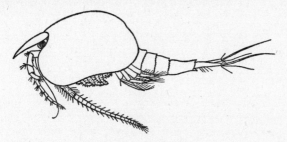

46. LIVING LINK WITH ANCIENT SHRIMPS. Although related to crabs, *Nebalia bipes* shows some of the primitive features of shrimp-like crustacea from the earliest fossil-bearing rocks.

on account of their completely aberrant nature, then this sequence of classification can be described in simpler terms as follows. First, we have the primitive shrimp-like forms; next, the ostracods, with bivalve shells; then the more advanced but still shrimp-like Copepoda. These are entirely unknown as fossils, but the bodies of the living species are small, delicate and not suitable for preservation in the rocks, except in unusual circumstances, such as those which produced the Rhynie Chert. Nevertheless, basing the opinion mainly on the study of the anatomy and comparing this with what is known of other living fossil crustacea, it is generally accepted that they are primitive and represent survivors of an ancient group. Finally, there are the Malacostraca, represented by woodlice, lobsters and crabs. Included also in the Malacostraca is the primitive group of Phyllocarida, with its genus *Nebalia*, which are in many respects intermediate between the Malacostraca and the Branchipoda. Forms resembling *Nebalia* are found in the Paleozoic, first in the Cambrian, and, more abundantly, in the Ordovician and Silurian. Even without such an intermediate the links with the past are still strong for the Malacostraca. The woodlice, freshwater shrimps and sandhoppers (Isopoda and Amphipoda) are derived from a shrimp-like type having a brood-pouch, and some of the Isopoda of the Jurassic are not

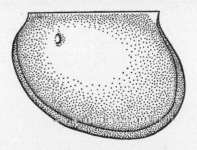

47. AN EXTINCT BIVALVE CRUSTACEAN: the
Ostracod *Leperditia* from the Silurian, over 300 million
years old.

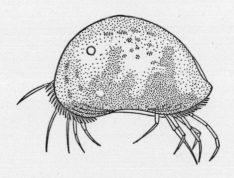

48. A LIVING OSTRACOD (*Cythere lutea*): compared
with the remains of *Leperditia* (fig. 47) there is comparatively little change in 300 million years.

very different from those living today. Further, the earliest
undoubted true prawns are found in the Upper Jurassic; and
some of these have thoracic legs similar to those of a primitive
family (the Acanthephyridae), the existing members of which
are now confined to the deep seas. A few more indications of
the generally old age of the Malacostraca are as follows. The
genus *Cancer*, which includes our edible crab, dates from the
Eocene. The affinities between crabs and lobsters are strength-
ened by a fossil crab from the Great Oolite of Wiltshire, which
is preserved with the abdomen partly extended, suggesting that

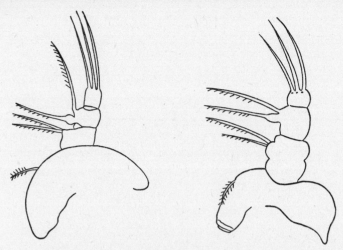

49. REMARKABLE PERSISTENCE OF A SINGLE
FEATURE: mandible palp of *Lepidocaris rhyniensis* (left)
on extinct crustacean from the Devonian compared
with that of a living crustacean, *Chirocephalus diaphanus*,
especially of the bulb on the middle bristle.

this was less completely doubled under the body than in
modern crabs. And by the lobsters, which have another
possible link with the past in the resemblance of the freshly
hatched young to a form like *Protocaris*, of the Cambrian rocks.
Another group of the Malacostraca, showing strong links with
the past, is that of the Stomatopoda, the mantis shrimps, themselves specialised. Some of the shrimp-like crustacea of the
Carboniferous bear a strong resemblance to the mantis shrimps
in certain of their features, and recognisable mantis shrimps are
found in the Jurassic, while by Cretaceous times there were
forms so like those living today that they are referred to the
modern genus *Squilla*. And finally, in the Cretaceous of the
Lebanon, have been found the remains of larvae very similar
to those of living mantis shrimps.

Considerable space has been given here to what must appear
tedious details. This has been done advisedly, because to a large

extent pronouncements on the past history of the crustacea are apt to be based on, and delivered, in vague terms. It was necessary for us to establish that the Crustacea as a group are archaic, and that it is difficult to pick out any for special mention.

Naturally, such a classification of the Crustacea is an over-simplification, yet it does not depart substantially from the true and close comparison that can be made. Such departure as it may make is the result of two things. First, we may be very sure that the fossil record is incomplete. In fact, many fossil crustacea are known only from the carapace, the legs having been lost or preserved as fragments only, so that often the rela-tionships can be no more than guessed. Secondly, no evolu-tionary sequence ever is even and uniform. If we return to the rocket simile, the geological succession of the Crustacea may be said to consist of at least five showers of different coloured sparks, in which individual sparks from the earlier showers tend to mingle with the later showers. And when we draw our hypothetical horizontal line, what we have approximates very closely to the living crustacea and the classification into which they are set.

Not many of the Crustacea are, as we might expect, normally spoken of as living fossils, but there are some which, if not strictly entitled to this name, come very near to being so. It may be best then to consider them under four headings; those pre-sumed to have the greatest antiquity, those of a primitive kind which are living today in out-of-the-way places and especially in underground streams and wells, those that are relics of former seas now vanished or vastly altered, and those that can be best described as living will-o'-the-wisps. These classes overlap, and the best way of describing them is to concentrate on a few main types, examining the claim of each in turn on our attention.

Before proceeding with this, however, a word may be said of the nature of deep-sea faunas generally, with special reference to the crustacea. It is a convenient point at which to deal with

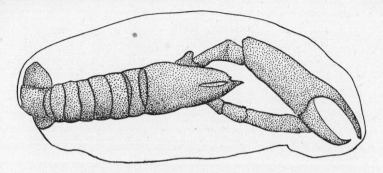

50. A FOSSIL LOBSTER FROM THE CRETACEOUS

the prevalent idea that deep-sea faunas are made up of archaic types which have migrated to escape competition. This dates from the early days of deep-sea exploration, when naturalists were first becoming aware of the rich fauna inhabiting the abysses of the ocean, which had until then been supposed to be barren of all life. It springs, in fact, from what would now be called "wishful thinking", for they confidently expected to find in the deep seas living representatives of animals known only from fossils, survivors from earlier geological periods. In other words, the hope of finding living fossils in the ocean deeps was based on the idea that the great ocean basins had remained unchanged for vast periods of geological time. The truth seems to be, as pointed out by the eminent palaeontologist Sir Arthur Smith Woodward, that the deep-sea fauna as a whole belongs to comparatively modern times; that the migration into the deep waters of the ocean took place in the Cretaceous. Certainly the number of deep-sea crustacea representing extinct groups is greater than in other phyla. The lobster-like Eryonidea, found today only in the deep sea, were known as fossils long before they were discovered as living animals. They are all blind, even the eye-stalks being vestigial. Another distinctive character is that the first four, and sometimes all five, pairs of legs end in claws. All other related crustacea, such as lobsters and crabs, have three pairs of such legs only. The fossil

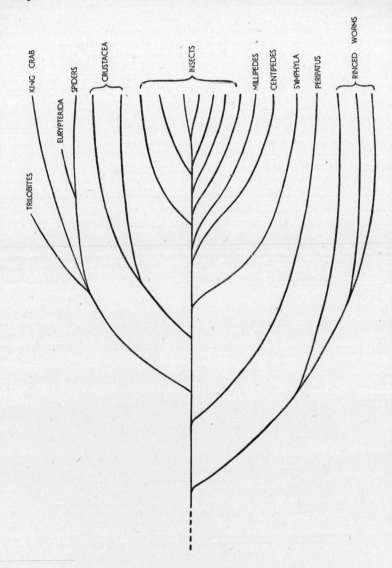

51. DIAGRAM SUGGESTING POSSIBLE LINES OF
EVOLUTION AND RELATIONSHIPS OF WORMS AND
ARTHROPODS. (The group insects, as shown here,
includes also the Collembola, Protura and Diplura.)

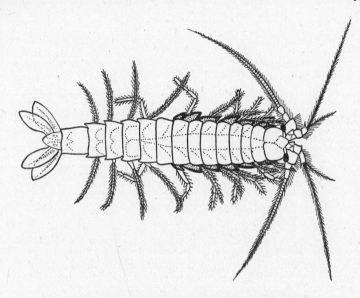

52. MOUNTAIN SHRIMP OF TASMANIA: *Anaspides* has
found a secure retreat in out-of-the-way streams.

Eryonidea are found in the Secondary Period, from the Triassic
to the early Cretaceous. Some had well-developed eyes, and
probably lived in shallow water, like those preserved in such a
perfect state in the lithographic limestone of Solenhofen, which
appears to have been laid down in a lagoon. No fossil Eryonidea have been found since the early Cretaceous, and it is
assumed that at about that period they migrated from shallow
waters into the deep seas, and that their descendants have persisted there until now.

The deep-sea family of crabs, the Homolodromiidae, also
show affinities with certain fossil forms. In the deep seas also
are found members of the hermit crab family, perfectly sym-
metrical and showing no sign of having adopted the habit of
living in mollusc shells, as the shallow-water hermits do, and
from this it is usually assumed that they are primitive.

Deep-sea Crustacea are surprisingly like those found in

shallower waters, and the number showing primitive characters is comparatively small.

We may go further and say that it would be surprising if
there were no archaic survivors among the crustacea of the
deep seas, since, on land and in the fresh waters, the most
archaic types have been found in out-of-the-way places. For the
classic example we must again go to Australia. In 1892 there
was discovered in the rocky pools of mountain streams in
Tasmania a crustacean to which the name mountain shrimp
(*Anaspides tasmaniae*) was given. An inch and a half long,
brown in colour, it resembled a prawn, except for the absence
of a carapace and the complete division of the body into
segments. At first sight there is little remarkable in it. The
importance of its discovery lay in the strong resemblance it
bore to a number of remains found in the Carboniferous and
the Permian which had until then proved puzzling.

These creatures resembled the shrimp-like forms, but in the
absence of a carapace and in the division of the thorax into
segments they recalled the modern woodlice and freshwater
shrimps. Since these are the features found in *Anaspides*, it
was assumed that the mountain shrimps of Tasmania were the
survivors of an ancient group, to which the name Syncarida
was given. Then came the discovery of two further living
genera: *Paranaspides* from the Great Lake of Tasmania, and
Koonunga from freshwater pools near Melbourne, Australia.
In addition, more complete remains of a fossil, *Praeanaspides*,
had been found in the coal measures of Derbyshire. W. T.
Calman, in his *Life of the Crustacea*, comments: "There can
be little doubt that the Syncarida arose during the Carboniferous epoch (or earlier) from primitive shrimp-like forms which
lost the carapace; but after flourishing for a relatively brief
period, the group dwindled away, although a few survivors
have lingered on, like so many other 'living fossils' in the
isolated Australian region."

Dr. Calman had made a special study of the Crustacea, but
it would seem that part of this statement gives too little weight

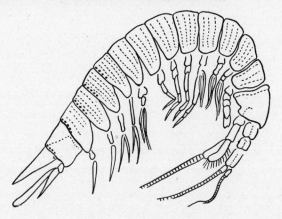

53. AN ANCESTOR OF THE MOUNTAIN SHRIMP from the coal measures of Derbyshire.

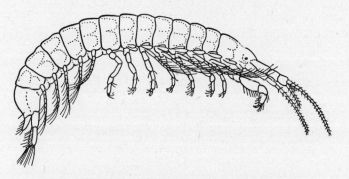

54. A RELATIVE OF THE MOUNTAIN SHRIMP:
Koonunga from the freshwater pools near Melbourne, Australia.

to the known distribution of other archaic survivors, which today are world-wide in their distribution. It could be that 250 million years ago the ancestral Syncarida enjoyed a similarly wide distribution, which the imperfection of the fossil record tends to obscure. It may even yet prove, as we shall see, that modern Syncarida are more widely spread than we at present suppose.

One of the living crustacea giving point to this remark and, incidentally, offering a highly interesting story in its own right, is the brine shrimp (*Artemia salina*). Common all over the world in the evaporating pools of salt-works, the brine shrimp will stand a very high salinity, such as few other animals can tolerate. Until 1848 it could be found in the salt-pans at Lymington, in Hampshire, where the water contained as much as a ¼ lb. of salt to a pint of water. It has, however, a curiously disconnected distribution. Dr. Robert Gurney, writing in 1949, has pointed out that:

> Though it is able to live in water from about 6 per cent to about 25 per cent of salt, the exact conditions requisite for its existence are unknown. For example, in Egypt it abounds in salt-pans at Port Said, which draw their water from the sea, but it was not found in any of the brine-pools that adjoin the Bitter Lake, although these contained other animals, and some of them were quite salt enough for *Artemia*. It was not simply a question of the source of the water or proximity to the sea, for Denham and Clapperton (1826) found it in salt lakes at Fezzan in such immense numbers that the natives, who called it *Dud*, made it into cakes for food.

While there is only one morphological species all over the world, *Artemia* varies much in form in different places and in different degrees of salinity. Gurney points out that at Cagliari males are as numerous as females and reproduction is always sexual, and in these individuals there are invariably forty-two chromosomes in the nuclei of the cells. But at Capodistria there is another race in which no males have been found and reproduction is always by parthenogenesis. In this race there are 148 chromosomes and the individual shrimps are about twice as large as those from Cagliari. Similar differences are found in other races. Such chromosome differences would be impossible to detect in fossil forms. Thus the last part of the story of the brine shrimp illustrates merely one of the difficulties

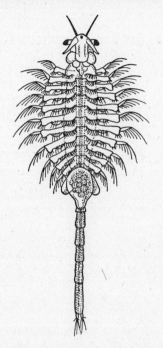

55. BRINE SHRIMPS survive in waters of very high
salinity; their occurrence is, however, sporadic.

of making comparisons between fossil and recent animals,
especially where these are invertebrates.

From the depths of the ocean, from high up in the mountain
streams, and from highly saline pools and lakes, the story of
crustacea relics takes us to wells and underground waters. One
of the species now assigned to the Syncarida, together with the
mountain shrimps of Tasmania and Australia, was discovered
in a well at Prague in 1882, and was given the name of
Bathynella. A second species of this genus was found in 1927,
in the Bath Stone quarry at Corsham, in Wiltshire. It was one-
twenty-fifth of an inch long and it is presumed to be living in
the water in rock crevices—where, in other words, only
accidental discovery could reveal its presence. The first species

appeared again in 1912 and has since been found in wells
and underground waters in several places. *Parabathynella* has
been found in places as far apart as Yugoslavia and Malaya.
All these are survivors of a group whose history goes back at
least 250 million years.

A large proportion of such finds are from southern Europe
and the Mediterranean region. The blind prawn of Galilee
(*Typhlocaris galileaea*), up to three inches long and colourless,
was originally found in a large spring near Lake Tiberias.
Later, it was taken from a deep well near the coast. Gurney
reports that when he visited Lake Tiberias in 1924, after the
spring had been cleaned out, he could find no trace of the
prawn, but it was there again in 1938. From this he presumed
that it was widespread in the wells and underground waters of
that region. The nearest relatives of the prawn are marine. Two
other species of this same genus were subsequently discovered,
one in a cave near Benghazi, another in a cave in southern Italy.
Gurney writes:

> To understand the distribution of the species of *Typhlocaris*
> we have to suppose that their common ancestor must have
> been widely distributed in the early Tertiary period, perhaps
> 50,000,000 years ago, in the surface waters of a land that
> then stretched unbroken from North America to Asia
> Minor. Owing to climatic and earth changes the species
> died out except in places where it could adapt itself to life
> underground, and in the long period of isolation the separate
> colonies have changed so that they are now distinguishable
> as new species. It is surprising that, after such an enormous
> lapse of time, the differences are not very much greater. If it
> takes so many million years to make a species, imagination
> reels with the effort to grasp an idea of the time necessary to
> evolve all the diversity of creatures which have peopled this
> earth.

In England a blind water-woodlouse was discovered in 1925
at Ringwood, together with a blind shrimp, some copepods and
a species of water-flea which has also been taken in Switzerland,

Germany, France and Belgium—all survivors in fissures in the chalk since preglacial times. In Herzegovina, in 1923, a giant freshwater shrimp was discovered, two and a half times the size of the ordinary freshwater shrimp. It is related to an even larger shrimp, half as big again as the Herzegovina giant, found in Lake Baikal, which has been there since Tertiary times.

Our knowledge of these stragglers is, as can be seen from the infrequency of their occurrence, far from complete. Life in the underground waters ensures a constant temperature, an absence of drought conditions, and abundance of food, for they have been found to contain a great many vegetable particles on which freshwater shrimps and other small crustacea feed. The fact that these are present underground is clearly demonstrated when artesian borings are made. A variety of animals may be thrown out in the water from far below, these being usually the same as can be found in the waters at the surface. Thus, the subterranean fauna may not only have received new recruits in times past but is probably still receiving them from the surface waters. In the favourable conditions obtaining deep underground, their survival over long periods of time is made a strong possibility.

The last two examples belong to the Branchiopoda, the subclass usually regarded as representing the most primitive of the living crustacea. They are the fairy shrimp and a form known as apus. These are two of the forms earlier described in this chapter as having a will-o'-the-wisp character. The fairy shrimp, up to an inch long, is almost transparent and colourless, remarkably beautiful and graceful in movement. On each side of the head is a large black eye; running through the body the intestine can be seen tinged with green; and the hind-end of the body bears a pair of red-tinted tail-tips. The body bears no carapace, and is segmented throughout, the first eleven segments bearing pairs of fin-like legs, and the remainder of the segments being free of appendages. The animal usually swims back downwards, with a rhythmic movement of the legs,

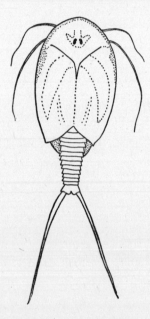

56. LIVING FOSSIL WILL-O'-THE-WISP: apus lives
in ponds that periodically dry up and its occurrence
is sporadic.

feeding on minute particles of organic matter floating in the
water, the movement of the legs causing food-bearing currents
to flow towards the mouth. High-speed photography has
shown that one of the several lobes on each leg functions somewhat like the screw of a ship, with an independent semi-
rotary movement, the pitch of which can be altered to keep the
shrimp stationary, to go backwards or forwards, to move fast or
slow, without interfering with the food-gathering operations of
the legs as a whole.

The fairy shrimp lives in small pools, temporary puddles and
in water in cart ruts, and although it has been fairly often
recorded in this country in recent years, it seems to have the
habit of appearing and disappearing unexpectedly. Living in
waters that are likely to be dried up in summer, it escapes

larger predators such as fishes. It is enabled to do this by the fact that its eggs, which are capable of remaining alive for about six months, lie dormant in the mud, ready to hatch when heavy rains return.

The second will-o'-the-wisp was formerly known by the scientific name of *Apus cancriformis*. By the rules of zoological nomenclature this must now be replaced by the name *Triops cancriformis*. Since, however, the animal has long been known as apus, the name being used as a common name, there is fortunately a tacit agreement to continue this practice. The first published record of apus is dated 1732, but the first specimen recorded for Britain was 1738. The second record was in 1816, the third in 1850, and then nothing was seen of it until 1907. The first three finds were at Bexley in Kent, Christchurch in Hampshire, and at Bristol respectively. The fourth was at Kirkcudbrightshire, in Scotland, but although the same ponds were visited the following year no apus was found. It was found again in Hampshire in 1934, 1947, 1948 and 1949, and also in Kirkcudbrightshire in 1948.

Apus belongs to an order of branchiopods, the Notostraca, which are sometimes called tadpole shrimps. The body is covered above with a broad shield-shaped carapace, having something of the appearance of the print left by a horse's hoof, and from under the rear margin of this shield, the segmented body extends backwards to end in a pair of long whip-like appendages corresponding to the tail-tips of the fairy shrimp. Apart from the rarity of its appearance, apus is of outstanding interest in relation to the geological history of the crustacea. It is usually assumed that the extinct trilobites were closely related to the crustacea, indeed, that the latter may have sprung from a trilobite ancestor. There were, however, crustacea-like forms contemporaneous with the trilobites in the Cambrian period, and one of these, *Protocaris*, looks very like the present-day apus.

CHAPTER IX

INSECTS AND GONDWANALAND

THE evolution of the Insects so far as it is known, is closely linked with the history of the former continents, Gondwanaland, Laurentia and Angara. Several species are living fossils in the strictest sense. These will be dealt with later. There are, in addition, whole groups of insects which have survived relatively unchanged for a long period of time. The causes of survival form a necessary subsidiary to our discussion, and the past history of these groups has much to contribute to it. The oldest perfect remains of insects known are from the Devonian, although certain impressions of wings from the Silurian have been said to be those of a primitive bug. But by the Carboniferous the number of insects had increased, with cockroaches and mayflies, up to four inches across the wings, particularly in evidence. In the Upper Carboniferous, essentially an age of ferns and of insects, there were dragonflies with a wing-span of two feet, mayflies twenty-eight inches across, and cockroaches in plenty, conspicuous for the number of species recorded, some 200 being known. Thereafter, the following sources of information are particularly noteworthy: the Lower Permian beds of Kansas, in the U.S.A., and the Upper Permian beds of the U.S.S.R. and of N.S.W., Australia; and Australia's Ipswich beds, of the Triassic period. Insects preserved whole in amber, although beautifully preserved and, for this reason, often spectacular, are comparatively modern. For example, many species of ants preserved in this way for 40 million years can be assigned to genera still extant.

Altogether more than 10,000 species of fossil insects are

known, but comparatively few of these, except for the ones preserved in amber, are known from complete specimens. Usually, the fossils consist of parts only and mainly of the remains of wings. In 1952, however, Dr. L. S. B. Leakey reported having found a number of fossil invertebrates in the Lower Miocene of Kenya. These included a caterpillar which, in spite of its soft-bodied nature in life, had retained its natural shape in a quite surprising manner. More, possibly, than most animals, insects are identified and classified on their external form. Even where the complete insect has survived as a fossil, all too often parts of it, or even the whole, have been crushed and distorted. Nevertheless, we can be sure that dragonflies and mayflies are well represented in the Primary rocks, and that beetles form a dominant group in the Secondary and Tertiary rocks, although their remains cannot be so readily identified except where embedded in amber.

In spite of these difficulties, it still may be said that the lines of evolution of the various groups constituting the class Insecta have been followed out fairly satisfactorily. To achieve this, two methods have been used. In the case of the earlier rocks, the Paleozoic, there is the direct evidence from fossils. For the Secondary, or Mesozoic, and for the Tertiary, it has been necessary to rely mainly upon evidence deduced from the geographical distribution of present-day species. Once these species are classified they can be taken group by group and, on the basis of which characters are considered primitive and which advanced, the species can be arranged in what appears to be their evolutionary sequence. This, combined with what is known of the actual Mesozoic and Tertiary fossils, gives a fairly satisfactory picture of the more recent past. So, with direct evidence from the fossils themselves in the Primary rocks, and those of the Triassic (including the famous fossiliferous beds already referred to), the continuity can be reasonably well maintained down to the present day. In such a study, the knowledge of the movements of the land masses assists and corroborates.

As was stated in the Introduction, in the Cambrian period the large land-mass, the so-called Gondwanaland, covered what is now South America, Africa, parts of Australasia and Antarctica, together with the intervening seas. This continued more or less throughout the Ordovician, Silurian and Devonian periods. By the beginning of the Carboniferous, the area of Gondwanaland had increased slightly, while in the northern seas, smaller areas which had been just recognisable in the Cambrian period had increased to form two continents, Laurentia, extending approximately from central North America to western and central Europe, and Angara, covering what is now north-eastern Asia. During the second half of the Paleozoic period, at least, these three continental areas were relatively undisturbed, for long periods, by upheavals of the land or encroachments from the sea. Under these conditions terrestrial life had the maximum opportunity to develop undisturbed. By contrast, the seas between Laurentia and Angara in the north and Gondwanaland in the south, were subject to changes which affected vastly their flora and fauna.

Although these continental territories themselves were relatively stable, there were considerable variations of climate, taking place gradually and over long periods of time. This appears to have caused migrations of whole populations of animals from one area, which was becoming unfavourable, to areas where climatic conditions were becoming favourable to them. Thus, the climatic changes influenced indirectly the evolution of new faunas, or the redistribution of existing faunas. The climate also influenced their evolution in another, more direct way. In Laurentia, for example, the weather in Carboniferous times was sub-tropical and the insect fauna included, in addition to the cockroaches and dragonflies, such forms as the now extinct Paleodictyoptera, insects which passed from the larval to the adult stages without an abrupt meta-morphosis. The Paleodictyoptera, incidentally, were regarded by some authorities as a more or less direct off-shoot of the Tribolite stock, a view now no longer held. In Gondwanaland,

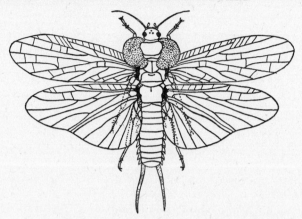

57. RECONSTRUCTION OF A FOSSIL INSECT: *Lematophora typica* from the Permian has wing flaps in front of its normal wings. (Compare *Hemiodoecus* fig. 61.)

on the other hand, where the climate ranged from temperate to cold, insects tended to develop a metamorphosis, with a pupa. This enabled them to tide over the winter, as with so many of the temperate species today.

By the end of the Permian period, Laurentia had become a tropical desert and at the same time Gondwanaland had grown warmer, so that the climates of the two were tending to equalise. The land-bridge between them had become more pronounced, making possible an extensive mixing of their respective faunas. This may have been helped by the Permian Ice Age which, for part of its duration, affected Gondwanaland, causing migrations of some of the insect populations. All of the Paleodictyoptera had died out in Laurentia by the end of the Paleozoic, and their place was taken by insects which spread northwards from Gondwanaland into Laurentia. The majority of cockroaches survived. There is also evidence that at this same time there was a migration of reptiles and the earliest mammals from Gondwanaland northwards. The result was that at the beginning of the Mesozoic, the insect faunas all over the then land-masses were a mixture of elements from the Gondwanaland fauna and survivors from Laurentia. The continent of Angara received its whole insect population from Gondwanaland. Thus, the entire insect population of the world became a mixture of species having a direct development, emanating mainly from Laurentia, and of species undergoing a metamorphosis, derived mainly from Gondwanaland. With the subsequent break-up of the Continent of Gondwanaland, the further evolution of insects into smaller and specialised groups took place. In general, therefore, the Gondwanaland and the Laurentian lines of evolution date from the Paleozoic and those of Angara from the Cretaceous. And following the migrations and mixings already noted, the stage was set for the evolution, during the Mesozoic and the Tertiary, of the present-day insect fauna of the world.

The most primitive group of insects living today is assumed to be the Collembola, with its earliest representatives in the Rhynie Chert of Aberdeenshire, Scotland, typified by the species *Rhyniella spraecursor*. The Collembola constitute one of three orders of a sub-class, the Apterygota, or wingless insects, the other two orders being the Protura and the Thysanura. To avoid misunderstanding, it is necessary here to make the clear distinction between the Apterygota and the so-called Aptera. This last name is now no longer in use, but it was formerly used to include insects, such as lice and fleas, that have secondarily lost their wings. Moreover, it is not without interest at this point to examine the reason for this distinction between the two kinds of winglessness, and the evidence upon which it is made. This can best be done by a brief examination of the present classification and the principles upon which it is based.

The class Insecta may be divided into three main groups:*

* In more up-to-date classifications of insects, the Collembola, together with the Protura and Diplura, are excluded from the class Insecta and form classes on their own. This is expressed in the table on page xiii. For the sake of convenience, the classification used in most text-books is retained for purposes of discussion.

58. INSECT REMAINS IN THE PERMIAN ROCK: the fossil *Permoscytina* bears a "tail", of unknown function, which persists in one of its living descendants. Pattern of a wing impression (bottom right) revealed by expert examination.

the Apterygota, already noted, and the sub-classes Exopterygota and Endopterygota. The Apterygota are mostly of too small size to be familiar, living among dead leaves, under stones, bark and in other out-of-the-way places. They never show any traces of a wing, either in the adult or during the development stages. There is no metamorphosis, and even the adult resembles the more familiar insects at an immature stage. A noteworthy feature of the structure of the Apterygota, except those known as Diplura, lies in the mouth-parts, which consist of a pair of mandibles, almost exactly like those of Crustacea, and a pair of processes that are unlike anything found in other insects, except mayflies. In addition, the body is distinctly segmented, which recalls the condition found in Peripatus and the annelid worms, as well as in archaic arthropods, such as the Eurypterida.

The Exopterygota may be exemplified by the cockroaches, although the group also includes earwigs, locusts, crickets, termites, mayflies, dragonflies and the various bugs. Many of the species in this sub-class are vegetarian, but some, like the dragonflies and praying mantis, are carnivorous. In all, the three segments of the thorax are readily distinguishable, and the abdomen is almost invariably composed of ten segments, with two short stiff tails at the hinder end, the cerci or cercopods. The cercopods are of significance because they resemble so closely comparable structures in the Crustacea, and are therefore usually counted as primitive. Except in dragonflies and mayflies, there are two pairs of membranous wings, the front pair thickened and closing over the larger and thinner hind pair, which are folded under the front pair when the insect is at rest. In some species, of course, the wings have been lost secondarily. The last important characteristic concerns the development, and it is from this that the sub-class derives its name. The outward appearance of the growing insect changes slightly with each moult, but it is only the mature insect that possesses functional wings. On the other hand, the wings slowly develop throughout the lifetime of the individual, and their rudiments are at all stages to be seen on the outside (exo=outside). Finally, there is no metamorphosis, there are no abrupt changes from the larva—grub or caterpillar—to a pupa, and thence to the imago, or perfect insect.

The Endopterygota, which includes butterflies and moths, beetles, ants, wasps and bees, flies and mosquitoes, are characterised by a marked metamorphosis in the life-history, the abrupt change from the larva through the pupa to the perfect insect. And, as the name implies, the developing wings are internal, although their position may be marked externally during the pupal or chrysalis stage by ridges on the outer skin.

The entomologists studying living insects, comparing the internal structure and the general form of the body, especially of the mouth-parts, early came to the conclusion that those insects now placed in the Endopterygota were more advanced in the evolutionary scale and must have come into existence more recently than the Exopterygota. These last they regarded therefore as the more primitive. In the same way, they came to the conclusion that the Apterygota were the most primitive of all. The general view they adopted may be summarised briefly

as follows. The most primitive insects are the bristle-tails or
Thysanura, which possess certain structures that can only be
interpreted as inheritances from an ancestral stock. At an early
period in its development the typical insect embryo passes
through a stage in which it has five pairs of appendages on the
head. In addition to this, the body consists of fifteen segments,
with a pair of limbs to each segment except the last. As
development proceeds, all the body appendages excepting
those on the first three segments and on the fourteenth—these
last corresponding to the cercopods in the Exopterygota—tend
to disappear. From this, they presumed that the ancestral insects
must have been somewhat like the Symphyla, a group of
centipede-like animals, having five pairs of appendages on the
head, the back covered by fifteen or sixteen dorsal scutes, with
a pair of long cerci extending backwards from the hinder end
of the body, and moving on twelve pairs of legs. This
transitory phase in the embryo of the typical insect contains,
therefore, the strong suggestion, if not actual evidence, that the
ancestral insects and the ancestors of the millipedes and
centipedes must have had much in common, and probably
sprang from the same stock.

There is less evidence for the ancestors of insects having
sprung from the extinct group of trilobites, although there must
have been a close relationship between them. There is perhaps
more evidence of a close relationship between the ancestral
insects and the ancestors of some of the Crustacea. It is sometimes assumed that the insects are descended from some wood-
louse-like ancestors which had crawled out on to the land at
a very remote period of time. All this is, however, very
hypothetical, although the facies so presented is probably
fairly near the truth. We are on much surer ground in seeking
an affinity between the ancestral insects and the Symphyla,
especially through those insects belonging to the order
Thysanura, including *Campodea* and *Lepisma*, the silverfish,
which have a number of features in common that are not found
in the rest of the insects.

Although, as already stated, these conclusions have been arrived at largely by comparing living insects, there was some evidence from the fossil record to uphold, or even, perhaps, to suggest them. Even so, they are confirmed by the evidence obtained subsequently from fossils unknown at the time when the original conclusions were taking shape. A particular example of this will be mentioned later. Meanwhile, it will be sufficient to recall that the more complete fossil record we have today also gives, in general terms, a greater antiquity for the Exopterygota than the Endopterygota. Thus, we have cock-roaches, dragonflies and mayflies, all members of the Exoptery-gota, predominant in the coal measures of 250 million years ago, and beetles, belonging to the Endopterygota, pre-dominating in the Mesozoic, 75 to 195 million years ago.

If any living insects are to be regarded as living fossils, it must be especially the members of the Apterygota, the bristle-tails and the springtails. Unlike the typical living fossil, represented by one or at most a small group of species, as in tuatara and peripatus, and having a restricted distribution today, the Apterygota are found all over the world and are represented by a large number of species. Instead of describing one or a few species as has been done for tuatara and peripatus, it is necessary to describe the group Apterygota as a whole, and to make particular reference to one or two typical species. In other words, they are more to be compared with the marsupials in the manner of their persistence, but are even more widely distributed at the present time.

The first of the three orders of Apterygota, the Protura, comprises minute slender-bodied insects, seldom exceeding 1·5 mm. long, and usually coloured a yellowish-brown. They are commonly found, often in large numbers, in the lower layers of the moist ground litter of forests, in sphagnum moss, under stones or loose bark. The abdomen, in the adult, consists of twelve segments, segments nine to eleven being added after hatching. This process of post-embryonic addition to the body segments, known as anamorphosis, is characteristic also of

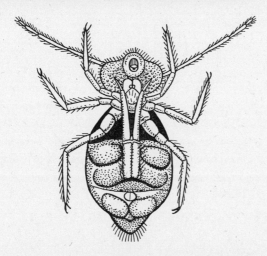

59. ONE OF THE EARLIEST INSECTS: springtails are more widely distributed over the world than any other insect.

millipedes and centipedes, but it is not found in any other insects. Considering the very small size of the Protura, it is not surprising, although unfortunate from the point of view of our knowledge of them, that no fossils of this insect order have been found.

The next order of Apterygota, the Collembola, or spring-tails, is more widely distributed than any other kind of insects. Springtails are found throughout the world, even on the continent of Antarctica. Usually they live in decaying vegeta-tion, in leaf-mould, under loose bark and similar places. Some are aquatic, some live on the surface of water or even on the surface of snow. Larger than the Protura, they range from 1 to 10 mm. long. Many are dark in colour, being black, dark brown, purple or blue; a few are white, and some of the dark-coloured forms are marked with yellow or bronze. The body is clothed with numerous small bristles or with scales. Locomotion is normally by a slow crawling movement, but in many species the body is provided with an apparatus for springing—a forked tail, usually turned forwards under the body, which, when released, springs back striking the ground and causing the insect to leap into the air. Most springtails have no tracheae, and in those possessing such breathing organs they are restricted to a single pair just behind the head. Although a few species are predaceous, and some live on the higher plants, the great majority feed on decaying vegetation, on fungi, lichens, pollen, diatoms and other lowly forms of plant life. To all appearance, therefore, they have preserved the dietetic requirements that could have been satisfied by the vegetation growing on the land in Paleozoic times.

In contrast to the Protura, a few fossil springtails are known, being of especial interest. Others have been found embedded in amber. One fossil springtail, together with those in the Rhynie Chert, found in Canada, has a pair of divergent stylets at the hinder end of the body which suggest that the "spring-tail" is a later development from "tails" comparable to those found in the next order, the Thysanura.

The habits, as well as the general structure of the Thysanura, or bristletails, the third order of Apterygota, do not differ markedly from those of the two preceding orders, except that whereas the Protura and Collembola require a damp habitat, many Thysanura can live in dry situations. Very small insects, they live in leaf-mould, under stones or loose bark, in the soil, and in the nests of termites and ants. Some have become commensal with man, feeding on starchy substances, in bread bins and in the bindings of books and in the paste used for fixing wallpapers. These are the well-known silverfish. All have long thread-like tails extending backwards from the hinder end of the body, or else have a pair of terminal pincers. Another characteristic is that most of them have four pairs of spiracles on the thorax leading into tracheae. Relatively few fossils of Thysanura have been found. Those preserved in amber are indistinguishable from, or very closely related to, species living today.

Although the Apterygota are generally accepted as the most

archaic representatives of the class Insecta, it must be confessed that this is based almost exclusively on the evidence afforded by species living today. This can, however, be interpreted as a very strong argument for considering them archaic. Thus in his *Monograph of the Collembola and Thysanura*, published in 1873, Lubbock epitomises his findings in the words: ". . . the genus *Campodea* must be regarded as a form of remarkable interest, since it is the living representative of a primaeval type, from which not only the Collembola and Thysanura, but the other great orders of insects, have all been derived". Although writing in so dogmatic a tone, Lubbock had to rely mainly on his deductions from modern insects. Some of these have been satisfactorily corroborated by subse-quent discoveries in the fields of entomology and palaeontology, and especially by the discovery of *Rhyniella praecursor* in the Rhynie Chert of Aberdeenshire. Although this last species is founded on remains of the heads only, these are sufficiently distinctive to leave little doubt that they represent archaic Apterygota, and almost certainly fossil Collembola.

If we may accept the Apterygota as living fossils, then there is the added interest that the class Insecta provides the only living fossils commonly found within human habitations. These are the cockroaches, the silverfish and the firebrat. The second is sufficiently commonly seen for a brief description of it and of its habits not to be out of place.

The silverfish is nocturnal in habit but may sometimes be seen by day, especially if disturbed, scurrying rapidly away. Its spindle-shaped body, bearing a pair of long thread-like antennae in front and three long thread-like tails behind, is silvery white, with a yellowish tinge on the antennae and legs. Including antennae and tails, it may have a total length of up to half an inch. The silvery appearance is due to the body being covered with minute shiny scales. The female lays from seven to twelve eggs, which hatch, according to temperature and other conditions, in from six to sixty days. The young silverfish resemble the adults but are only a twelfth of an inch long and, in the early stages, lack scales. They moult several times before becoming adult, reaching maturity in no less than twenty months, a remarkably long time for so small an animal. The silverfish is a very inconspicuous insect in an obscure habitat, but one holding great interest for the biologist.

Even although the Apterygota have been presented here as living fossils, it is readily apparent, as, indeed, was pointed out earlier, that they do not come into this category in the usually accepted sense of it, nor is their case as clear-cut as, say, that of tuatara. Rather, we have the probable survival from extremely early times of whole groups of archaic insects, the Collembola from the Devonian and the cockroaches and the dragonflies from the Carboniferous. This persistence through time with so little alteration of whole groups of animals which still flourish exceedingly and appear likely to do so for a long time yet, seems linked with the spectacular viability of the class Insecta as a whole, for nothing could be more remarkable than the tremendous number of species in that class, as compared with other groups of higher animals. The general principles that may here be involved must be considered later, together with any conclusions and comparisons to be drawn from animals already discussed or about to be discussed. For the moment, we must limit our discussion to the Apterygota and some of the Exopterygota.

The first comment to be made is that, in all these cases, the diet of the archaic survivors seems to be vegetable and, especially, decaying vegetation. Thus, at all times, from the Pre-Cambrian onwards, the food supply presents no problems. Secondly, it should be mentioned that the habitat is not specialised, and is also one that gives the maximum of shelter and, possibly, of protection from predators. It may also be that living among dead leaves, under stones and bark and in similar situations is likely to provide the most favourable and also reasonably constant conditions of temperature and humidity. Thirdly, attention can be drawn to another aspect of the problem, the significance of which is not immediately

60. A LIVING FOSSIL IN THE HOME: silverfish are
one of the few living fossils found in houses.

apparent, and, indeed, may not necessarily be an operative
factor. This is, that the change in climatic conditions over the
continent of Laurentia, in Paleozoic times, which brought
about the extinction of several groups, such as the Paleodictyoptera, allowed the bristletails and the springtails as well as the
cockroaches, or rather their ancestors, to continue unscathed.
This suggests that these insects have a wide toleration of
temperature and other climatic changes. Finally, it is worthy of
mention that where the length of life of the individual is known
it appears to be relatively extended, as in the silverfish, and,
whether justified or not, there is the temptation to link this with
the known longevity of such things as tuatara and tortoises,
which are also archaic survivals. In other words, it may be
that an operative factor in the survival of the group, whether
family, order or phylum, may be the ability of the average

individual to enjoy a long span of life. Probably the most striking is the seventeen-year cicada of North America, which is not only the longest-lived insect but is also one of the more primitive living today.

In contrast to the surviving groups of insects so far discussed, there are those known from a few specimens or groups of species bearing a close resemblance to early fossils. The leaf-hopper *Darthula hardwickii*, for example, has peculiarities of structure, including a long "tail" of unknown function, found also in the Permian fossil *Permoscytina kansasensis*. The hairy cicadas of Tasmania and south-eastern Australia, especially associated with high altitudes, sheltering under bark by day and flying out only at night, are very closely related to Permian fossils from the U.S.S.R. Then we have a small group of scorpion-flies represented by a few species in the eastern U.S.A., Chile and Western Australia, sole survivors of insects known from the Lower Permian. Perhaps the most instructive is the family of primitive sucking-bugs, the Peloridiidae, comprising "the rarest and most remarkable of the Hemiptera (i.e. bugs) and which may well be descended in an almost direct line" from the original ancestral forms. The family is especially important for the light it throws on the distribution of the land-masses in the southern hemisphere in former times.

In the *Australian Journal of Science* (1941), Dr. J. W. Evans comments:

> It is probable that no student of the geographical distribution of animals and plants nowadays doubts the past occurrence of an Antarctic continent that linked together South America, New Zealand, Tasmania and Eastern Australia. If, however, any doubt should still exist, the evidence contained in the present distribution of the Peloridiidae should go far towards removing it. These insects cannot fly and could not be carried alive in any stage of their life-cycle by wind, sea or other agencies. Their present distribution is evidence not only of certain land

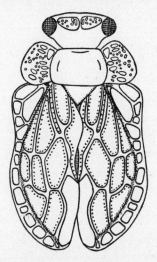

61. A FLIGHTLESS INSECT WITH A REMARKABLE
STORY: *Hemiodoecus fidelis*, one of twenty-five insects
found in Australia, of the family Peloridiidae, which
suggest that Australia and Antarctica were once
joined by a land-bridge.

connections of the past but of a former widespread uniformly
wet, though not necessarily cold, climate, that must have
extended over a large part of Eastern Australia.

In his account of the history of Peloridiidae, Dr. Evans
gives us an excellent example of how the evidence is slowly
pieced together. The first specimen was collected in the forest
at Puerto Toro, in Terra del Fuego, in 1897, and was named
Peloridium hammoniorum. Ten years later a second specimen was
found under a decaying tree-trunk in the forest around Punta
Arenas, Magellan Straits. In 1924 two related specimens, an
adult and a nymph, subsequently named *Xenophyses cascus*,
were found in leaf-mould in a forest in North Island, New
Zealand. At about the same time, a nymph collected on Lord
Howe Island and two adults from Tasmania, belonging to
another species, *Hemiodoecus leai*, were discovered in the British

Museum collections, and three years later a further search brought to light an additional specimen of *Peloridium hammonio-rum* which had been collected in Argentina in 1900. In 1932 three specimens of another species were found in Queensland. Four years later another was found in a private collection in Melbourne, Victoria. In 1937, twenty-five specimens of a further species were found in Tasmania. So the knowledge of the Peloridiidae was built up, and it became apparent that they were always associated with beech trees; further research showed that they lived not on the leaves but in moss having a similar distribution to the beech trees of South America, Australia and New Zealand.

The insects are only 3 mm. long and unable to fly, since they lack hind-wings, and the fore-wings are reduced to a varying extent. There could be little doubt that their presence in Patagonia and in Australasia was due to a former land-bridge, probably across Antarctica. Alongside this it has been found that the nymphs of the Peloridiidae have many primitive characters in the structure of the head. Above all, the adults, although lacking hind-wings, have wing-like flaps on the first segment of the thorax. In modern insects, wings are borne on the second and third thoracic segments, but a number of Paleozoic insects had in addition wing-like flaps on the first segment. The Peloridiidae are the sole surviving insects to retain such flaps which are undoubtedly homologous with wings.

CHAPTER X

A PERSISTENT MUD-DWELLER

U P to this point the insistence has been mainly on animals that do not live in the sea. Since life began there, and if the lower invertebrates were the first forms of animal life to appear, then we should expect their modern descendants to show many examples of living fossils. That, indeed, is true, and the examples of persistence shown by the lowest of animals is just as remarkable as anything we find in the higher animals. They are, however, unsatisfactory from several points of view. First, we have the fact that the bodies of so many of the lower invertebrates, such as jellyfishes, sea-anemones, worms, and the like contain little in the way of a hard skeleton to be preserved as fossils. Secondly, since they have persisted in a simple form over so long a period of time, it follows that there has been little progress and comparatively little change. Thirdly, such changes as there have been, and of which we have precise knowledge, cannot be described except at great length. It can be said, however, that the broad pattern of their evolution is no different from that found in the higher groups of animals. We find them already in existence in the earliest Paleozoic rocks, differing in no great degree from the forms living today. From there we can trace the main stems, some of which die out during the Paleozoic, while others live on into the Mesozoic. These main stems send off branches, some to die out and others to flourish and increase in strength and numbers down to the present day. And there are the instances in which a main stem flourishes and then dies out except for a slender line of descent that comes down to us, virtually unchanged, through the ages.

Within this pattern, common to all the main groups of

animals, we can see two types of living fossils: those that linger on, represented today by one or a few species, or a few groups of species; and those which, while showing little more in the way of change than the lingerers, are represented by many species, often distributed all over the world and, in a biological sense, as flourishing as any newly evolved forms. Among the arthropods we have the contrasting examples of the king-crabs, representing the lingerers, and the cockroaches and dragonflies that are still flourishing. Or we may cite peripatus to be contrasted with the widespread and very numerous truly wingless insects, the Apterygota, including the well-known silverfish. In reptiles, we can contrast the lingering tuatara with the still-flourishing tortoises and the crocodiles. The fishes offer us the contrast of the lungfishes or the coelacanths with the flourishing sharks and rays. Apart from anything else, this makes for enormous difficulties in classification, and, where there is no fossil evidence to guide us, we find ourselves left with the odd species or groups of species having no obvious connection with any of the main groups. It also brings out strikingly that merely to be higher in the scale does not mean that one animal is better fitted to survive than another; or to put it the other way round, fitness to survive is not necessarily based on a progression from a lower to a higher form of organisation.

There is one further point that emerges, but first a word may be said about the attainment of large size in the lower invertebrates. Much has been made of this throughout the preceding chapters, and it appears almost a rule that gigantism marks a zenith in evolution. It is necessary now to qualify this. Some mathematically minded biologists claim that theoretically there is no limit to the size an organism can attain in an aquatic medium. Like any other generalisation this contains a germ of truth and no more. There is, nevertheless, a greater tendency to the attainment of large size by aquatic organisms without it necessarily being a symptom of impending decline. Yet the picture is confused, for our limited knowledge of large invertebrates, fossil or recent, does not permit our reaching firm conclusions. We can, therefore, do no more than enumerate a few examples in the hope of obtaining a general idea of the meaning of size in aquatic organisms on the one hand, and terrestrial organisms on the other. The largest land animal was the Diplodocus, eighty feet long; but most of its length was taken up with the long tapering tail and the long slender neck. The largest aquatic animal—so far as we know—is the 100-foot blue whale, whose bulk is far superior to that of Diplodocus. On the other hand, the largest crabs and lobsters are not outstandingly big, nor are aquatic insects noticeably larger than those living on land or in the air. Crabs, lobsters and insects have an external skeleton, however, which places a physiological limit on size whether in water or out of it. Where there is no skeleton, or none worthy of the name, as in squid or octopus, or where the skeleton is internal, as in fishes, we find not only giant species, but also the occasional individuals of a species that grow to a much larger size than the maximum normal for the species. Eels will often attain a large size when, for any reason, they fail to join the spawning migration, and giant individuals have been recorded among both marine and freshwater fishes. Coming back to the lower invertebrates, there is nothing to show that corals of former times were any bigger than they are today, while larger sponges are fished up today than have ever been found fossil. Against this, we know that corals tend to break up after death, under the pounding of wave action, and sponges disintegrate so that their remains do not necessarily indicate the original size of the animal.

While on the question of giant size, mention must be made of the giant Australian earthworm which may reach up to twelve feet long when fully extended. The meaning of this giant in the scheme of earthworms is not clear, but, rightly or wrongly, one cannot help linking its presence in Australia, the home of so many relics, with the possibility that it is a monstrous survivor.

Two things can be said on this question. Theoretically it may be true that there is no limit to the size an aquatic organism can attain, given freedom from accident or disease, but there is in practice a maximum for any given species beyond which it cannot function. In land animals, which, among other things, have not the advantage of a supporting medium to help carry the weight of the body, the practical limit of size is more readily reached. In them, it is more reasonable to base conclusions on a comparative study of maximum body size. In aquatic organisms, especially those living in the sea, giant individuals, quite apart from giant species, can be expected to a greater extent than in land animals.

To return to the general discussion, the pattern of evolution is well exemplified by the marine invertebrates belonging to the phylum Brachiopoda, or lamp shells, which are exclusively marine. The typical lamp shell has its soft body enclosed in a hinged bivalve shell, one half of which is larger than the other. This larger valve ends in a beak projecting beyond the hinge, and through a hole in the beak passes a fleshy foot to anchor the animal to the substratum, usually a rock or coral. The lamp shell has a general resemblance to a Roman lamp, the beak being the counterpart of the spout of the lamp. Internally, the most conspicuous part of the soft body is a pair of ciliated loops or arms. Brachiopods feed on minute organisms and organic particles by opening the shells to take in water, the cilia on the arms then extracting the food particles. Their mode of life is extremely simple, therefore, and at all times there is an abundance of food, for as long as there is life there will be subsequent decay.

There are two branches of the lamp shell phylum, those that have been called here the typical lamp shells, in which the shell is limy and hard and the foot short, and those that have a horny shell and a long foot or stalk. Both share the simple mode of life and both always find an abundance of food. Both are marine, and both presumably came from a common ancestor. Yet, in the limy shelled forms there has been

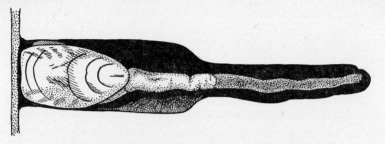

62. THE PERSISTENT LAMP-SHELL: *Lingula*, which
has survived relatively unchanged since very early
times, lives in a burrow in the mud.

persistent change throughout their history, whereas in the
horny-shelled forms there has been little change. The latter are
represented by the genus *Lingula*, which has persisted relatively
unchanged throughout hundreds of millions of years. The
difficulty is to explain why one branch of the family shows
little change while the other branch shows perpetual change.
We might argue that because *Lingula* lives in the mud, within
a burrow that may be anything up to a foot deep, changes in
the environment do not impinge on it to the same extent as
they do on the limy brachiopods. If there were such a ready
explanation, then we should not expect to find the coelacanth
fishes showing so little change when in the course of 300
million years they have moved from a freshwater habitat to the
sea, and from the shallow seas to the deep seas. Indeed, we
must presume that there may have been physiological or
functional changes in the coelacanths without perceptible
changes in structure. We should also need to find some other
reason for the unchanging form of the common jellyfish
(*Aurelia aurita*) which is widely distributed throughout the
seas of the world and yet is nearly constant from one habitat to
another, such changes as there are being usually in behaviour
rather than in structure.

Not only did the limy lamp-shells alter continually in form
but they reached a zenith in numbers of species, in abundance

of individuals, and in the maximum size attained, after which they went slowly into decline, as their history shows. Both the horny and the limy lamp-shells are found in the earliest Paleozoic rocks, the Cambrian. In the Ordovician they were the commonest animals in the shallow seas. In those times the limy lamp-shells were much the more numerous of the two forms, and their shells were often ornamented with radiating ribs. In the Silurian, the limy-shells were so profusely abundant that their empty shells formed whole beaches; today these are preserved as rock formed almost exclusively of shells embedded in a cementing matrix. By the end of the Paleozoic, most of the species found earlier in that period had died out, but the number of limy brachiopods as a whole was still undiminished, new forms having arisen to replace those that had disappeared, and these were often more ornate than their predecessors. Among such new forms are those recognisable as the ancestors of forms later to appear in the Mesozoic rocks. But the end of the Paleozoic was the end of their period of tremendous prosperity. New forms continued to arise, new shapes were assumed, but their numbers were showing a marked decline. Over 2,000 species have been recorded from the Silurian rocks. The number of species living today is barely 150.

There is almost a sparkle about the history of the limy brachiopods: the tremendous rise in number, the rapid changes in form, the ornamented shells; then, the final fall into obscurity, for they are now unfamiliar even to the zoologist, and it is something of a rarity to find one in a haul of the dredge or the trawl. This spectacular career contrasts with that of the horny-shelled brachiopods. Several forms of these are known, but the most familiar is that already referred to, *Lingula*. Found in the Cambrian rocks, never so numerous as the limy-shelled relatives, showing only slight changes in form throughout the 500 million years that have passed, without extravagant ornament to its shell, this branch of the lamp-shells has persisted through the ages. Today, *Lingula* is found on the shores of Japan, the Indo-Pacific islands and Queensland, Australia;

63. LAMP-SHELLS WITH HARD SHELLS: a living
lamp-shell (left) and one of the extinct forms with
heavily ornamented shells.

although restricted in their range, they are sufficiently numerous
to be eaten in large quantities in several localities of this range.
By contrast, anyone depending for sustenance on the present-
day limy-shelled brachiopods would suffer from acute
malnutrition.

Another thought comes uppermost at this juncture. In
the Cambrian rocks we find the lamp-shells already fully
developed, both the limy-shelled and the horny-shelled forms;
from then on, for 500 million years, they continue, the one
virtually unchanged, the other showing changes but still
recognisable as a limy-shelled brachiopod. That is, it has not
undergone any spectacular changes. Admittedly, the early
strata of the Cambrian period follow on the Pre-Cambrian
period, for which almost the whole of the fossil record has
been lost; and it could be that the catastrophes that had
eliminated practically all the other kinds of fossils had also
eliminated the ancestral lamp-shells. But the story is the same
whether we are dealing with a line of evolution that started in
the Silurian, Devonian, or even much later periods such as the
Cretaceous and the Eocene. At one horizon in the rocks a
particular organism is not there; a step forward in time and
there it is showing a full development and continuing to give
rise to other forms, or else continuing unchanged; but whatever

its subsequent fate, it shows no changes so marked as those that would have been necessary to bring it into being from a pre-existing form.

Professor F. A. Schilder has made an analysis of the number of species of fossil and recent Mollusca, and has come to the conclusion that there has been "a specific change of fauna every 15 million years". The first fossil mollusc is 600 million years old and in that time there have been forty changes of fauna, through which such forms as *Lingula*, the nautilus and *Spirula* have persisted.

So the pattern of the living fossil, and of all such lines of evolution, is of a living animal with a long lineage stretching back to the earliest rocks, represented intermediately or not by numerous fossils. The first known fossil is substantially like the last and like all those in between, and all are substantially like the living survivor. All differ in slight details of shape and size, and these are marked by assigning the various forms to different species or even different genera. To the quick glance, or for that matter to the sustained examination of the inexpert eye, these species and genera are often indistinguishable, but to any eye they are readily recognisable as lamp-shells, king-crabs, or what you will. We are in no doubt as to their identity. There is, in fact, less difference between the various species and genera of king-crab, or the various species of horny-shelled lamp-shells, than there is between the many varieties of dogs produced from the original dog-stock by human selection. There is, therefore, reasonable justification for saying that *Lingula*, *Limulus*, and all the rest, have persisted for millions of years unchanged. The one thing almost invariably missing is the link binding it with the stock from which it sprang.

If the origins of these lines of evolution are so obscure, how can we be so sure that they have originated as offshoots from already existing stocks? To avoid technical explanations, it is better to take as our example here the king-crabs rather than the lamp-shells. If, now, we examine closely all the known species of king-crabs and compare them with what is known of other invertebrates, we can say with confidence that they have more in common with the Arthropoda than with any other group of animal. We may go further and say that they are more nearly like the true crabs, on the one hand, and the spiders, on the other, than the insects, or the millipedes and centipedes. In almost precisely the same way we can see resemblances between all domesticated dogs and the wolf, jackal and fox, on the one hand, and the seals and the sea-lions on the other. These are things that anyone, whether trained as a biologist or not, can appreciate. Jonstonius, in the sixteenth century, had no hesitation in calling his specimens of *Limulus* the *Cancer mollucensis*, the crab from the Moluccas. To him they were crabs, as they were to those who first called them king-crabs. The fact that we cannot trace their ancestors is no more surprising than the fact that nobody can be sure of the ancestor of the domesticated dog, and yet it must have died out since man first started to domesticate animals. We can accept, therefore, that the king-crab is one of the Arthropoda, and that it did not come into being spontaneously any more than did the domestic dog.

Continuing our search, we find there are many points of similarity, not always obvious to the untrained eye, between king-crabs and the extinct trilobites. This viewpoint is further strengthened when we find that the larvae of the king-crab look remarkably like young trilobites in outward form. Other supporting evidence can be found in anatomical details, all of which lead to the same conviction, that king-crabs, trilobites, spiders, true crabs, and insects, all arose from a common ancestor. Even so, the fact remains that such a conviction is based upon analogy, that there are no fossils to fill in the gaps. The hunt for the missing links goes on, with extraordinarily little success. In instance after instance we can trace an animal back through the fossil record, but we always arrive at a point where the animals are in existence and just beyond that nothing can be found of them.

The size of the gap varies, naturally. In some groups it is smaller than with either *Lingula* or *Limulus*. The smaller the group we are dealing with, the smaller, as a rule, is the gap between it and what we suppose to be its ancestral stock, until we come down to the studies of living forms. In them, by dint of very close study, we can obtain an almost complete picture of the way the smaller subdivisions, the subspecies and the races are budding off from a central stem. This is dependent, however, on having not only the whole animal to examine, its skeleton, soft parts, colour and the rest, but also a knowledge of its habits and habitat, as well of its general behaviour. Most of these things cannot be deduced from fossil remains. That we can trace such things in living animals, however, leads us to believe that if all the data were available the same thing could be done for extinct species. Further, the fact that the gap is narrower with the smaller sub-divisions and becomes, generally speaking, wider with the larger sub-divisions, is also encouraging. The upshot of such studies is to suppose that the initial steps in the evolution of animal groups are passed through rapidly, that the whole process occupies a relatively short space of time, and that it takes place within a limited area.

Reference has already been made to the Tree of Descent, and it may be useful to push this botanical analogy still further. In the growth of a tree, we start with a period of germination, during which nothing appears to be happening. This is succeeded by a period, the seedling period, of rapid growth and maturation. After that, growth slows down perceptibly and the tree, having thrown out its branches, shows little change over a long period of time, but there is just sufficient change for us to see it reach a maximum size and then go into decline. Just as this early rapid growth, the attainment of full stature, a long period of apparent standing still merging ultimately into a slow decline, finishing with a relatively abrupt termination of life, is applicable to individuals, so it seems to be true also for groups of individuals, whether species, genera, families, orders, classes or phyla. It is applicable to plant as well as animal life, indeed to all forms of living growth, so much so that although it brings us no nearer an explanation, we can with conviction say that it is an inherent property of living matter. And we may suspect that in matters of extinction or survival, this difference in viability is the main factor.

Before leaving what may perhaps appear an unnecessarily long digression, there is one more thing to be said. In comparing the successive early stages of development of a main group of animals, the comparison between it and the germination of a seed may not be so far-fetched as appears at first sight. If the findings of the geneticists are correct, it is possible for an individual, while undergoing no change in structure or habitat, to accumulate gene-mutations. Then, with a change in environment, these may take effect, leading to sudden and far-reaching changes in structure. There seems no reason why something comparable may not take place in groups of individuals, even to groups as large as phyla. It is probably along such lines as these that we may need to seek the explanation for the gaps between main stocks and those from which they are presumed to have sprung. Accumulations of gene changes suddenly becoming effective, for whatever reasons, could lead to the rapid proliferation of species, or to the sudden appearance of a single line of evolution or to any intermediate between these two. The rapidity of the changes, and the consequent short period during which they were effective, coupled with the already familiar difficulty of obtaining complete fossil evidence, would go a long way to explaining the existence of these gaps, if it did nothing else.

Another group of shelled animals demands our attention, and although the story it has to tell does no more than reiterate what has already been seen in one group after another, it is necessary to tell it if only for the sake of completeness. This group is the one known as the Mollusca. The two outstanding characteristics of molluscs are the protection of the soft body by an outer shell, built of layers of lime and a horny material, and the possession of a muscular foot. Molluscs are unlike the

other higher invertebrates in a number of ways: in the absence
of segmentation of the body, in the possession of a rasping
tongue or radula, and so on. This is putting the case in a very
simple form, however, for over the 100,000 or more living
species of molluscs, and the extremely numerous species of
fossil molluscs, every conceivable variation in the shape of the
shell and of the foot, and of the use to which either could be
put, will be found. In many the shell has become internal, or
reduced to a few granules of lime, or to a small layer of horn,
and the foot equally has undergone vast changes from species
to species and from one group to another. These things do not
concern us here, except in this summary form. Taken with the
plan of the anatomy, in all its variations, we have as usual in a
large phylum, almost infinite variation without the general
plan being lost in any of them. So we are able to say of any one
of its members, with little hesitation, that it is a mollusc. The
phylum is divided into three main types: lamellibranchs
or bivalves, such as oysters, mussels and clams, with a two-
valved shell, and the foot usually laterally compressed for
digging; gastropods, such as the snails and winkles, with a
coiled shell and a muscular foot for walking; and cephalopods,
including the nautilus, octopus and squid, with the shell
usually internal, the foot converted into a siphon for jet-
propulsion, and the head surrounded by a crown of tentacles.
Only sufficient details have been given to identify the groups
in what follows.

Mollusca are represented in the Cambrian by comparatively
rare fossils of bivalves and gastropods, and also of some creatures
which floated or swam and which may have belonged to a
sub-division of the gastropods, whose recent forms are known
as sea-butterflies; or they may represent ancestral cephalopods.
In the Ordovician, bivalves had not increased very much,
gastropods were fairly common and cephalopods had become
abundant. From then on, the picture is of the bivalves and the
gastropods, and especially the latter, gradually gaining the
ascendency, and the cephalopods taking a second place. There

64. A RARE SHELL OF ANCIENT LINEAGE: formerly
believed to be extinct, *Pleurotomaria* is a survivor from
Paleozoic times.

is no need to lay stress on the success achieved by the gastropods
and, to a more limited extent, the bivalves. During the course
of their long history they have given rise to large numbers of
species, some of which have died out, while others have gone
on to proliferate new species; generally, these two stocks have
burgeoned and blossomed to fill the seas and the fresh waters
and, in the case of the gastropods, the land, with abundant
forms and populations.

One of the most discussed of the gastropods is *Pleurotomaria*.
Its shells are found in the Paleozoic and it was believed to be
extinct until early in the present century, when a few living
specimens were found. Altogether five species are known, from
moderately deep water off Japan, the Moluccas, South Africa
and the West Indies. Two West Indian species are known
from six and four specimens respectively, and although the
Japanese species is better known it is still sufficiently rare to
form a prized possession of the shell-collector.

The cephalopods divided into two groups: those with two
pairs of gills and those with one pair. The latter are known
abundantly from the cigar-shaped fossils, called belemnites,
and from the modern octopus, squid and cuttlefish. The last
three are the most highly evolved of all the cephalopods,
although the number of their species living today is less than
1,000 compared with the 120,000 of the gastropods and

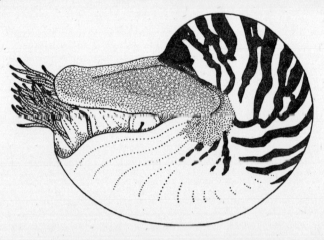

65. THE PEARLY NAUTILUS OF THE PACIFIC: a
surviving relative of the extinct ammonites.

bivalves. They are, nevertheless, highly successful and still flourishing. The groups having the two pairs of gills included the ammonites, which started in the Devonian with a simple straight shell. Then they increased enormously in numbers, reached a zenith and finally died out. Concurrently the shells became coiled, more and more richly ornamented, larger in size, in some species several feet across, till, finally, they tended to become simple again, less richly ornamented, or else became distorted; and the ammonites which finally died out by the end of the Cretaceous have gone back very much to their starting in so far as the shell is concerned. From this stock there is one survivor that has come down to the present day virtually unchanged, the pearly nautilus. It lives in the shallow seas around New Caledonia, the Fiji Islands and the Philippines, where it is caught for food.

While the nautilus is the most archaic of the living cephalopods, it is outrivalled in interest by the smaller *Spirula*, related to octopus and cuttlefish. Its shells are often found in great profusion on tropical and subtropical shores. Yet *Spirula* is known from very few living specimens, all damaged by the

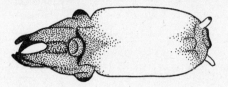

66. THE ANOMALOUS SPIRULA, related to the octopus,
is rarely seen alive today although its shells are common
on tropical beaches. *Spirula* has survived from
Paleozoic times.

nets in which they were caught, with the exception of one
caught by the "Dana" Expedition in the North Atlantic in
1921. This was actually seen swimming at the surface and
captured intact. The anatomy of the living *Spirula* appears to
be highly specialised, but its shell retains the form of the fossil
Spirula found in the Paleozoic rocks.

G. C. Robson has written:

> It has been thought that the Ammonite stock actually lost
> its old vigour and exuberance of growth and ultimately
> degenerated. It seems, however, more likely that this is a
> superficial view and that the whole group of Ammonites was
> not subject to this degeneration. In all probability they
> became extinct owing to some great change in their environ-
> ment to which they could not adapt themselves.

It is conceivable that a change in environment could, under
certain circumstances, cause the extermination of a species.
It would be difficult to believe in any one change in environment, or even a series of changes, that could bring about the
demise of a whole multitude of species scattered throughout
the seas the world over. It would be difficult enough to imagine
this happening on the land where the environment is less stable
than the sea. There seems something to be said for Robson's
"superficial view". Adaptability is surely a feature of youth,
and if it is possible to make so many comparisons between
both individuals and groups of animals, even though they be

tentative, there must be something in common with their behaviour. If adaptability be the prerogative of the youthful individual, it may also be a feature of the youthful species or phylum. And youth is usually followed by an increasing loss of vigour and exuberance, and a greater tendency towards degeneration. The truth is that we are far from being able to say why these mass exterminations take place. The best we can do is to speculate.

One of the prime difficulties in any such speculation lies in the incompleteness of the geological record. Earlier in this chapter, it was implied that the lower invertebrates were poorly represented in the fossil record. This is, as then suggested, largely true, although in certain strata the remains of corals and sponges, sea-urchins and starfish and others with hard skeletons are often relatively abundant, and it should not be forgotten how abundant are the remains of sea-lilies, the stalked forms related to starfishes. There must have been many, however, that are not represented at all. As a contrast with what is found in most rocks we may quote from *The Succession of Life through Geological Time*:

> . . . more than a hundred different kinds of soft-bodied animal, mostly floaters or swimmers, including various worms, have been preserved in the Burgess Shale (Cambrian) of British Columbia, Canada. This remarkable deposit probably accumulated in a depression of the sea-floor where the water was stagnant, and where no scavenging animals or bacteria could live. The perfect preservation is unique among fossils; even hair-like appendages and digestive systems have left clear traces.

This shows what may yet come to light in other formations.

CHAPTER XI

THE LIVING COELACANTH

THE remains of fishes that have died out during the last 300 million years are sufficiently abundant for the course of evolution of the class as a whole to be well-known, and to anyone but a specialist the picture is too complex to be fully comprehensible. Briefly, during the Paleozoic and early Mesozoic times several major groups arose, some to die out, others to leave their dwindling survivors to persist until the present day. The sharks and their relatives, the skates and rays, may have dwindled in numbers, but they are still quite numerous. And, indeed, all fishes living today, including those more newly arrived on the scene than the sharks, are still essentially the same as they were 70 million years ago. Fishes, then, as a whole, are practically all living fossils. If we abide by our definition of a living fossil as an organism that has survived beyond its era, and if we accept the Devonian period, which ended nearly 300 million years ago, as the Age of Fishes, we are almost compelled to look upon every fish alive today as a living fossil.

Such a remark must, however, not be taken too literally. The purpose in making it is to emphasise the difficulty of keeping to exact definitions. Here, for example, the inconsistency relates to the term "Age of Fishes". Whereas the Age of Reptiles represents the period in the earth's history when reptiles were not only the dominant vertebrates on land but had reached the height of their development, the Age of Fishes was that period when the forerunners of fishes were the dominant vertebrates. The true fishes had in fact not yet appeared. The remark also draws attention to the difficulty of deciding which examples

will most enhance our discussion. It may be best to confine
our attention to the lampreys and hagfishes, the lungfishes and
the Coelacanth.

The earliest known vertebrates appear in the Ordovician,
and their fossil remains are thus some 400 million years old.
They were fish-like and heavily armoured, the body being
covered with bony plates. These Ostracoderms, as they are
called, abounded in the freshwaters 300 million years ago.
None was of great size, the largest being five feet long, and
although they had most of the characteristics of the typical
vertebrate, their outstanding feature was that they lacked jaws.
It is not known for certain how they fed, but it is assumed that
they scooped in accumulations of decaying matter, in a finely
divided state, from the mud on the river-beds. Towards the
end of the Devonian period the Ostracoderms began to decline,
becoming increasingly rare, and lost their armour. Today they
are represented by the lampreys and hagfishes, which although
they have a spinal column do not possess vertebrae in the true
sense of the word.

Lampreys are eel-like, without the paired fins so familiar
in the true fishes, but with median fins. In front, there is a
terminal sucker-like mouth. When at rest a lamprey attaches
itself to a stone by this sucker. Within the sucker are numerous
horny teeth, the larger of which are borne on the tongue. To
feed, it lays hold of a fish by the sucker and bores its way into
the flesh. The head also contains a pair of eyes, and a single
nostril on the upper surface. On each side of the head is a row
of seven gill openings, which appear to have been mistaken in
the past for eyes. Another interesting feature is a small yellow
spot on the top of the head, where the skin is thin and un-
pigmented. Beneath this is the third, or pineal eye, to which
fuller reference has been made in dealing with the tuatara.

Lampreys are caught in considerable numbers attached to
fish, but what happens to them while they are in the sea is very
little known. After spending some time in the sea, lampreys
ascend the rivers to spawn, and having done so die. The

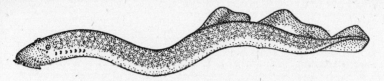

67. THE SEA-LAMPREY, living representative of the Ostracoderms of the Devonian period.

internal organisation of lampreys, while it has some special features peculiar to its class, is nevertheless that of the typical vertebrate, although obviously of a low order and therefore presumably to be labelled primitive. The brain and nervous system lie above the digestive tract and underneath what passes for a backbone. The brain is of lowly organisation although showing many of the basic features of the vertebrates. The two outstanding features of the animal, and those that interest us most here, are the skeleton and the development of the larva.

The skeleton consists of a notochord, or stiff rod, running from the skull to the hind-end of the body. Lying just behind the skull and beneath it is a cartilaginous basket for the protection of the gill-chambers. The notochord is composed of large vacuolated cells embedded in a protein secreted by themselves, the whole enclosed in a fibrous sheath, the turgidity of the cells keeping the rod stiff. The sheath surrounding the notochord is continuous with a layer of connective tissue which surrounds the spinal cord. Throughout its length the notochord is also supported by nodules of cartilage or gristle, and these, in the region of the tail, become joined to form a continuous plate, with rods of cartilage extending upwards and downwards from it into the fins. The skull is formed by a group of incomplete boxes, also cartilaginous, housing the brain and the organs of special sense, and in front are more cartilaginous rods and bars forming a skeleton to support the suctorial mouth. The basket protecting the gill-chambers is also formed of cartilaginous bars. The basis of the skeleton is therefore the notochord, and in the cartilaginous supports associated with it we see the beginnings of the vertebrae, the fin rays, the skull and the gill-arches of fishes; but there is no bone.

The heavily yolked eggs of the lamprey develop rather in the manner of those of a frog. After some three weeks they hatch; the larva, or ammocoete, as it is called, is at first trans-parent but later grows opaque. This eel-like larva lives in the mud at the bottom of the river, feeding on microscopic particles of decaying organic matter, seldom coming out except to change its feeding ground. Water is taken in through the mouth, which is not suctorial as in the adult, but is covered with a hood. The water passes out through the gill-slits, but not before the particles of food have been trapped in slime given off by a glandular sac lying in the floot of the pharynx. This is known as the endostyle. The slime with its enclosed particles is passed on to the intestine and digested. The ammocoete finally changes into the adult; and one important feature of this change, significant in the study of the higher vertebrates, is that the endostyle changes into the thyroid gland. The full signifi-cance of this is not yet fully understood, but it is of interest to note that extract of this thyroid injected into tadpoles will hasten their metamorphosis into frogs.

Hagfishes are entirely marine, and like lampreys are confined to the temperate regions of both hemispheres. They feed by entering the mouths of dead or dying fishes and eating the flesh, leaving only a bag of skin containing the skeleton. In certain respects hagfishes are more primitive even than lampreys, especially in the kidneys and the brain. In addition, they show a degeneration, as in the eyes, which are very small; and there is no pineal eye.

During the Devonian, when the Ostracoderms, the early ancestors of the lampreys and hagfishes were at their full development, the Placoderms and fishes also made their appearance. The Placoderms, with heavily armoured heads and bodies, died out towards the end of the Devonian, leaving few survivors which persisted for a short while only. It is possible that chimaera, the rabbit-fish, may represent a surviving

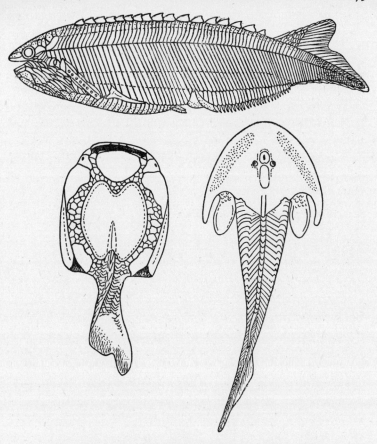

68. OSTRACODERMS FROM THE SILURIAN AND DEVONIAN, *Rhyncholepis parvulus* (top), *Drepanaspis gemuendenensis* (bottom left) and *Cephalaspis salweyi* (bottom right).

Placoderm, but this is uncertain. The true, or typical fishes, those whose descendants today form the vast majority of species with which we are familiar in the seas and rivers, also appeared in the Devonian period, and included the lungfishes. They had the body covered with thick enamelled scales. It was from the lungfishes that the terrestrial vertebrates appear to have

13

sprung. A little later, as measured in geological times, the first shark made its appearance, in the form of the primitive, stiff-finned *Cladoselache*, which reached six feet long. All these differed from the Ostracoderms—as their descendants differ from the Ostracoderm survivors, the lampreys and hagfishes—in possessing movable jaws. On the other hand, while the typical fishes developed a bony skeleton, the sharks, together with their relatives, the skates and rays, continued with a cartilaginous skeleton, which their descendants still possess today, although its structure shows a considerable advance on that of the lampreys and hags.

The sharks and skates are sufficiently well-known to need no introduction, and it will be enough to outline the main features in which they differ from the true or bony fishes, and to sketch briefly in what respects they show an advance on the lampreys and hagfishes. The shark, with its spindle-shaped body, with two sets of paired fins, median fins and vertical tail fins, differs from true fishes in a number of ways besides the possession of a cartilaginous instead of a bony skeleton. The gill-slits open directly on the surface, instead of being hidden under a gill-cover or operculum. The mouth is on the lower surface. The skin is covered with denticles instead of scales and the denticles have the structure of true teeth, with a pulp cavity surrounded by dentine and enclosed within an outer layer of enamel.

Internally the main thing to be noted is that the cartilaginous skeleton comprises a more complete box to enclose the brain, although the structure of this skull is still simple and has a large opening in the upper surface. The backbone is complete and composed of definite vertebrae. There is also an elaboration of the skeleton supporting the fins; or, in other words, the simple cartilaginous fin-rays, few in number in the lampreys and hags, form an extensive series in sharks and rays to support the median fins and the tail-fins. The paired fins are also supported by a cartilaginous skeleton, and this includes not only the fin-rays themselves but larger cartilages forming a support to the inner

69. A GROUP OF PLACODERMS OF THE DEVONIAN
PERIOD, *Pterichthys milleri* (top left), *Coccosteus
decipiens* (bottom left) and *Bothriolepis canadensis* (right).

half of each fin, so that there is a rough approximation to
the bones of the limbs and of the digits found in terrestrial
vertebrates.

The most significant thing about sharks, for our present
discussion, is their size. The earliest sharks, as we have seen,
attained a length of six feet. This was in the Devonian period.
During the ensuing Carboniferous and Permian periods
sharks were abundant in the seas, but they are known for the
most part only from their teeth and fin-spines. Some sharks'
teeth were enormous, those of *Carcharodon megalodon*, from the
Miocene, measure six inches high by five and a half across the
base. Their owners probably reached a length of sixty feet or
more. The largest sharks today are the whale shark, which

reaches a length of fifty feet or so, the basking shark, thirty-five to forty feet, and some of the large man-eaters, from thirty feet upwards. It is not surprising, therefore, that when a shark dies and, its decomposing flesh already falling from its skeleton, it is seen floating in the sea, or tossed about by the waves, or thrown ashore distorted beyond recognition, it should so often be mistaken for a sea-monster. There is, however, a more solid interest attaching to these large types. The two largest, as we have seen, are the whale shark and the basking shark, both of which feed on the microscopic plants and animals floating in the sea and known as plankton. It is common enough to refer to plankton as the Pastures of the Sea, even although there is a fair percentage of animal matter in it. Then, presumably, we are justified in referring to these large sharks as partly or mainly herbivores since they graze on these pastures. In spite of their huge bulk, however, their teeth are minute. The so-called man-eaters, on the other hand, which can be regarded as the carnivores of the sea, possess large cutting teeth. The enormous fossil teeth already mentioned belonged beyond doubt to carnivorous sharks, and some of these, as we have seen, are believed to have been sixty feet long.

It seems almost the rule, that where we have two sets of comparable animals, the one herbivorous, and the other carnivorous, the herbivores always attain the greater maximum sizes. This is certainly true for mammals, and we see it again in modern sharks. Whales show very similar differences. The blue whale, one of the large whalebone whales, reached a length of 100 feet, or perhaps more, before it became so intensively fished. The toothed whales, on the other hand, the carnivores, reach their greatest size in the sperm whale, which is known to have attained a length of sixty feet, with somewhat doubtful records of seventy-six and eighty-four feet respectively. Even if these larger sizes be allowed—and it is by no means certain that they can be relied upon—and if we allow the 120 feet equally unreliably recorded for the blue whale, we still have a maximum for the carnivores of approximately two-thirds the maximum for non-carnivores. This is about the same proportion that we have between the herbivorous whale shark and the man-eater. Similar differences in size can be seen between comparable groups of land herbivores and carnivores, with if anything a greater discrepancy.

Even if there were, in geological times, no larger sharks than *Carcharodon*, it might be that we have in it symptoms of what appears to happen in so many groups, the trend towards giant size followed by a decline. The sharks swimming in our seas today do not at first sight appear to be in decline, but the numbers of their species, as well as the numbers of their populations, are very small compared with those of the bony fishes. There is this further point; that some genera of present-day sharks are much older than those of true fishes. Even as early as the Upper Jurassic the Port Jackson shark, the monk-fishes and the guitarfishes were already in existence.

Lungfishes, on the other hand, are unquestioned examples of the living fossil. They look as if they ought to be extinct, and, indeed, are much nearer extinction than sharks. The surviving lungfishes, the ancestors of which reached their greatest development in the Devonian period, live in rivers, swamps or marshes. The Australian lungfish is found in two rivers only, the Burnett and Murray rivers of Queensland, Australia. The African lungfishes inhabit the river basins of tropical Africa over a wide area. The South American lungfish is confined to the area of the Amazon basin. The Australian species lives in pools that become low and stagnant in summer, and only occasionally rises to the surface to breathe. The other species, found in the swamps and marshes, rise at frequent intervals to breathe air. In the dry season, when the swamps and marshes dry out, they curl up and sleep at the bottom of a burrow, its entrance plugged with mud, but with one or more small openings to let in air.

In all lungfishes the external nostrils lie just above the upper lip and open behind into the mouth. In the African and South American species the opening into the throat is a slit-like

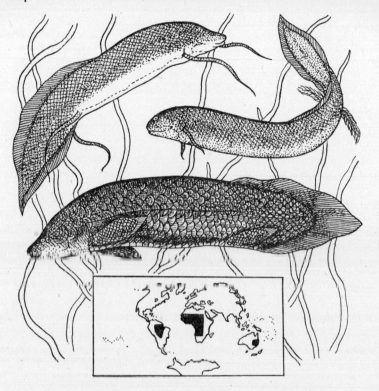

70. LUNGFISHES AND THEIR DISTRIBUTION TODAY.
African lungfish (top left), South American lungfish
(top right) and Australian lungfish (bottom).

glottis with an epiglottis, the glottis leading into a lung-like air-bladder. In the Australian lungfish this is single, and paired in the other two. The air-bladder is the counterpart of the swim-bladder in other true fishes, but it comes very near in structure to the lungs of higher vertebrates. Its walls contain muscle fibres and its cavity is divided into a number of compartments or alveoli. The blood-vessels of lungfishes are much more like those of the higher vertebrates than are those of the sharks and rays, or even of the other true fishes, and they make an especially close approach to those of the amphibia. There

71. FISH THAT MADE HISTORY: the living coelacanth,
rediscovered in 1938 after having been thought
extinct for 70 million years.

are other features of the anatomy which may be called advanced,
but alongside these there are many that are primitive. For
example, the notochord is persistent and forms the supporting
axis of the body, so that there are no vertebrae, and the skull is
partly cartilaginous and partly bony.

The last point to be emphasised is the distribution of the
lungfishes. This recalls the distribution of peripatus, of the
marsupials and of the living ratites, extending across the area
believed to be once occupied by the continent of Gondwanaland. On the other hand, teeth of a fossil lungfish of the
Triassic period occur in Europe, showing that the distribution
of the early lungfishes was much more extensive. It also empha-
sises the need, wherever possible, of linking our knowledge of
the past with that of the present, and vice versa.

Among the remains of fishes which are prominent in the
Devonian rocks, are those belonging to the Coelacanths. Until
1938 it was thought that the Coelacanths had died out in the
Upper Cretaceous after having persisted more or less unchanged for 230 million years. Then, just before Christmas Day
in 1938, a strange fish taken by a trawler off the mouth of
the Chalumna River, near East London, South Africa,

was found to be nothing less than a surviving coelacanth. In 1952, at about the same time of the year, Professor J. L. B. Smith, of South Africa, who had examined the first specimen and named it *Latimeria*, obtained a second specimen off the Comoro Islands, near Madagascar. The circumstances are sufficiently well known to need no re-capitulation. The second specimen was named *Malania*, but there is some doubt whether it was not the same as the first, with its fins injured, thus altering its appearance and giving the impression of being a different genus. This doubt is strength-ened by the finding of a third specimen, resembling the first but caught in the same area as the second. The fossil coelacanths varied in size from a few inches to five feet, and the living representatives measure five feet, which is contrary to what we generally find—the attainment of gigantic size preceding a decline.

Externally, *Latimeria* shows two peculiar features. The paired fins are borne on scaly muscular lobes instead of coming straight off the body, as in the more familiar fishes, and have the appearance of being halfway towards becoming walking limbs. The tail, too, is peculiar. Instead of the junction between the hinder end of the body and the tail fins being marked by a constriction, the body merely narrows rapidly and evenly and then continues backwards as a narrow strip dividing the rays of the tail fins into two equal parts above and below it. Beyond that is a small supplementary tail. Thus it shows the essential features of the fossil coelacanths. We know nothing yet of the internal structure, for the first living coelacanth was gutted before it could be examined by experts, and the results of such examination of the second specimen are not yet known. The chief peculiarity of the fossil forms, and one which may be expected in their living representatives, is that the air-sac was sheathed in bony scales and was therefore largely rigid. It could not have been a functional lung, as it now is in the lung-fishes; it must have had some other function. Owing to its rigidity, it is unlikely to have acted as a hydrostatic organ, as

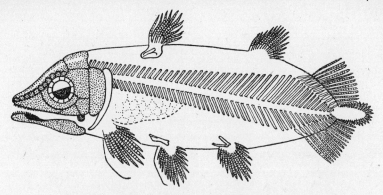

72. RESTORATION OF A JURASSIC COELACANTH
showing the peculiar structure of the tail.

in modern fishes, where the long membranous bag, known as the swim-bladder, contains a gas which can be adjusted to keep the fish buoyant at a particular depth. It is remarkable, however, that there is no passage from the nostril to the mouth. That the rigid swim-bladder had an important function there can be little doubt, since it is such a conspicuous feature in the fossils.

At the time that the second living coelacanth was found, there was much said, both in the press and over the radio, about the light its examination could be expected to throw on man's ancestry. It is doubtful whether this expectation will in fact be fulfilled. And to have labelled it a missing link, as was done, is wrong, for it does not connect two other types of known animals. On the contrary, the remarkable thing that emerges from a comparison of fossil and living coelacanths, so far as the outward appearance is concerned, at all events, is that there has been so relatively little change throughout the 300 million years of their history. It is, indeed, this very fact that makes for interest.

There is a tendency, among the lay public, when discussing such a living fossil as this, to speak of it as though the individual fish itself were very old. When the announcement was made public that a fish had been found that was believed to have been extinct 70 million years ago, this did not, of course, mean that this particular individual was 70 million years old. The probability is that it is only a few years old, and that the species as a whole has no greater longevity than any other fish. More-over, when we say that the fish survived relatively unchanged, it does not mean that there has been no change at all. As in all other living fossils, there have been constant, but small, changes throughout its history, but these changes have been so slight that we have no difficulty, at any stage, in recognising a coelacanth for what it is. This is the more striking since the coelacanths have so often changed their habitat. Their ancestors in the Devonian were marine, but in the Carboni-ferous they were living for the most part in the freshwaters. The coelacanths of the Triassic, on the other hand, had returned to salt water and were living in the shallow seas. As time went on, their descendants took more to the deeper waters of the sea. The usual idea is that with changes of habitat, of climate, and any other form of physical environment, structural changes emerge to produce new species. Here, however, we have relatively little alteration with a constantly changing environment. Pre-sumably, it is possible therefore to have adaptability without structural change. This is the real lesson afforded by the finding of *Latimeria*.

There is perhaps another striking lesson to be learned from the coelacanths as a whole. This concerns the actual collection of geological evidence. Thus, while the fossil remains of coelacanth fishes are comparatively rare in most of the rocks, they are sometimes found in great abundance. For example, when the foundations of a new building were being excavated at Princeton University, in the U.S.A., many hundreds of fossil coelacanths were dug out of Triassic rock. How far this reveals a local abundance of the fish in that spot, and how far it was due to peculiar circumstances surrounding the death of the fishes, or the preservation of their remains, is a problem that must remain for now. All such a finding does is to stress the

73. DIAGRAM SHOWING RELATIONS OF THE COELACANTHS TO OTHER VERTEBRATES AND THEIR DISTRIBUTION IN TIME

element of chance attending the collection of geological evidence. Equally, while there is a fairly continuous, if sparse,
series of fossil remains of the coelacanths, from the Devonian
to the Upper Cretaceous, there has been a complete blank
from there to the present day. Over a span of 70 million years
nothing whatever is known of their history. But the finding of
the living fish shows beyond a doubt that they have persisted,
and there is every reason to suppose that some day other fossil
remains will be found in post-Cretaceous rocks to fill in the
blank. This proof of the persistence of a given type when there
is nothing known of it in the available geological record, shows
that it is permissible to bridge huge gaps in time, as between
the living peripatus, say, and the Cambrian and Pre-Cambrian forms, even although geological evidence is entirely
lacking at the present.

Before leaving the fishes, a word about the causes of extinction may not be out of place. It has been suggested here that the
rich find of coelacanth remains at Princeton University may
have been due to unusual circumstances surrounding the death
of the fish, or it may have been due to lucky circumstances
assisting their preservation. It not infrequently happens that a
mass-death occurs, when thousands or millions of individuals
belonging to one species are killed. The Princeton coelacanths
may represent such a mass death. On the other hand, there is
little to suggest that, where they occupy areas at all extensive,
the extinction of any species may have been brought about by
some natural phenomenon, such as an earthquake, volcanic
activity or the like, or by a sudden change in climate. Such
events may produce mass deaths but not extinction, except
where a species is already nearing its end. The proof of how
much an animal species can endure is shown by the episode of
the tile-fish. Tile-fish belong to a family particularly well
represented in the tropical waters of the western Atlantic. In
1882, ships arriving at North American ports reported that the
surface of the sea was littered with dead and dying fish over an
area estimated at some 7,000 square miles. A billion tile-fishes

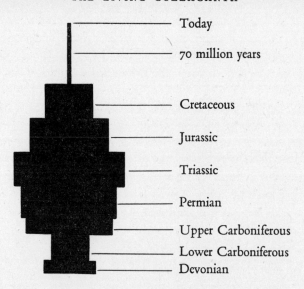

Today

70 million years

Cretaceous

Jurassic

Triassic

Permian

Upper Carboniferous

Lower Carboniferous

Devonian

74. HISTORY OF A LIVING FOSSIL: diagram showing the relative abundance of coelacanth fishes during successive geological periods.

are believed to have died and the species was thought to have been exterminated. The causes of this catastrophe are uncertain, but the general view is that unusually prolonged north and east winds driving cold water into the warm belt at the edge of the Gulf Stream had produced conditions in which the fishes could not survive. Be that as it may, the tile-fish were *not* exterminated. By 1900 they were being caught again and appeared to be present in abundance.

The episode of the tile-fish does not represent an isolated instance. This kind of event is always happening somewhere in the world. In a small way, we see it when a hard winter all but wipes out this or that species of bird, but the survivors hold on and in time the population is built up again to its former proportions. In another category, we have the near-extermina-tion of vast populations of insects by powerful insecticides, or of bacteria by antibiotics, leaving a residue which builds up a population resistant to the insecticide or the antibiotic, as the case may be. On a larger scale, we have had the decimation of the sponges of the West Indies, in 1938, by an unknown cause, probably a fungal disease; the sponges in question are still not extinct. As to the more spectacular natural causes, no volcanic activity could be more devastating than the explosion at Krakatoa, the effects of which were felt for hundreds of miles around. All life on the island was exterminated by the explosion, but as time passes, the populations of plants and animals are being slowly built up once more from neighbouring islands. Any endemic species would, probably, have been wiped out, but it is only in relatively confined spaces such as oceanic islands that natural catastrophes of this sort would result in complete extinction.

CHAPTER XII

THE MYSTERY OF THE RUNNING BIRD

I N Australia and the adjacent islands, as we have seen, there
is a complete marsupial fauna surviving from former times.
In South America there are also a number of species of
marsupials, and one in North America. To find out how the
only living marsupials in the world should have come to be in
two such widely separated localities, we must go back to
Paleozoic times when, as we have seen, the continental land-
mass of Gondwanaland stretched from what is now South
America, across Africa to Australia. By the Jurassic period,
soon after the first mammals had appeared, this land-mass had
begun to separate into two. To the west was Gondwanaland
proper, to the east, the newly formed continent of Australia
which had separated from it. It was not until the Eocene, when
Gondwanaland had undergone further division, that South
America and Africa were also completely separated. We
should expect Africa therefore to have had its share of the early
mammals, and it is reasonable to assume that at some time there
must also have been marsupials there. If Africa shared in the
early mammals, it must also have shared the other creatures
making up the Gondwanaland fauna, the birds, reptiles,
amphibia, fishes and so on; and, in point of fact, Africa is not
without its relics. There are, for example, lungfishes in the
Central Africa rivers, the only other surviving lungfishes being
found in South America and Australia. Africa also has her
species of peripatus, the only other surviving species being
found in the West Indies (close neighbours of South America)
and Australia. On the other hand, Africa has no living
marsupials, nor have any fossil marsupial remains been found

so far in spite of the extensive excavations within recent years, in East and South Africa. There are some mammalian relics however, such as the aardvark and the dassies, but they are few, both as to species and numbers of populations, and belong to the placental stock.

Africa is readily associated with ostriches, birds very like the rheas of South America and the emu and the cassowaries of Australasia. And when we think of these large flightless birds, we also think of the roc of Madagascar and the moas, as well as the kiwis, of New Zealand. It cannot be mere coincidence that these lands, which once formed the continent of Gondwanaland, should be the only regions where these flightless birds are now found. One might reasonably suppose that the relationship between these birds had already been settled. Birds as a class have been intensively studied for a century or more, and especially during the last half century. Yet it seems that, although much is known about their skeletons and plumage and a certain amount about their anatomy, there is no unanimity of opinion about the past history of these large flightless species or their relationship to each other.

To understand the points in dispute, we have to start at the beginning. The class Aves, or birds, is divided into two main groups: the Ratites and the Carinates. The Ratites are flightless birds, and include ostriches, rheas, cassowaries, emus, moas, kiwis, and the extinct *Aepyornis*, sometimes known as the roc. This group also includes the tinamous, of Mexico and Central and South America. The Carinates, on the other hand, include all the flying birds, together with those that, like the extinct dodo, the great auk, and a few others, are secondarily flightless. The Ratites are characterised by very weak wings and very strong legs, and by the fact that the breastbone is not keeled. The Carinates have strong fore-limbs, providing wings for flying, and the breastbone has a strong keel, to support the large muscles needed to work the wings. There are other differences, notably in the skull, the Ratites having the more primitive skulls. The tinamous are anomalous since they have skulls very like those of the ostriches, cassowaries, emus and the rest of the Ratites, but their breastbone is keeled as in the Carinates, and they are not flightless. They stand, therefore, midway between the two groups, and since nobody quite knows what to make of them, we can best ignore them in our present discussion.

Most people agree that birds are descended from a reptilian ancestor, and that at some point in the history of the stock their forerunners grew feathers instead of scales. There is also general agreement that the ancestral birds could not fly. In other words, that they grew feathers first, and afterwards learned to use them for flying. Then comes the paradox: the great majority of ornithologists who give any thought to the subject firmly believe that the Ratites are descended from ancestors that did fly. A very few ornithologists have been bold enough to suggest that the ancestors of the Ratites constitute an early offshoot of the main bird stock which grew feathers like the rest but never learned to use them for flying. Those holding such views have, however, been generally discredited.

Another unsettled question is how far the ostriches, rheas, cassowaries, emus, kiwis and the extinct moas and rocs are descended from a common stock. If we compare what we have seen in the marsupials with what we find in the Ratites, we are bound to conclude that all these birds are closely related, that they did, in fact, spring from a common stock. It seems difficult to believe, furthermore, that they ever did fly at any stage of their history; they were, in fact, in every sense of the word truly flightless birds.

The single species of ostriches, the largest living birds, have a rounded bulky body, long powerful legs and a long naked neck bearing an extremely small head. An ostrich may stand up to eight feet high and weigh 300 pounds, the males being larger than the females. The plumage of the male is black with white wing- and tail-feathers, that of the female a brownish-grey. The toes are reduced to two, one large and one small. The two species of rheas, living on the pampas and

14

scrub-covered plains of South America, are often called South American ostriches. In them the wings are larger and covered with long slender plumes. They have no conspicuous tail-feathers, the head and neck are fully feathered, and, as against the ostrich's two, they have three toes bearing large compressed claws. In addition to the similarity in their appearance, both ostriches and rheas lay a large number of eggs, the female ostrich laying fifteen or so, the female rhea laying a dozen, although they differ in that ostriches nest in pairs and rheas in groups. (These figures are necessarily approximate, owing to the disagreement of authorities on the subject.) In addition, ostriches have the trick of associating with herds of zebra and antelopes, and rheas with deer and guanacos.

Ostriches are placed in the order Struthioniformes and the rheas in the Rheiformes, but it has to be remembered that divisions used in classifying birds represent a finer distinction than elsewhere in the animal kingdom. Even so, it is possible that by placing the various groups of ratites in orders, instead of families, ornithologists have tended to lead themselves astray. Mammals as closely related as are ostriches and rheas would have been placed in separate families within the same order. To say the least, there is something inconsistent in doing this while, at the same time, placing both emus and cassowaries, more dissimilar to the eye than ostriches and rheas, in a single order —the Casuariformes—although admittedly in two separate families. There may be good technical reasons for these things. It may be that some peculiarities of anatomy justify it, but if we examine the matter in the light of past geography there seems a need to recognise a closer relationship than is implied by such divisions.

Emus and cassowaries are also ostrich-like, but have even smaller wings than their African relatives. The main difference between them and the ostriches is, however, that they have an aftershaft or accessory plume on each feather, as long as the main feather itself. There is only one species of emu, smaller than an ostrich, confined to Australia, with a mottled grey and

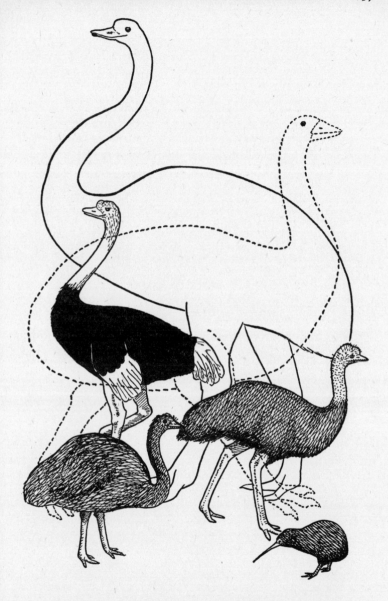

75. FLIGHTLESS BIRDS OF THE SOUTHERN HEMISPHERE.
In descending order of size: moa, *Aepyornis*, ostrich, emu, rhea, kiwi.

brown plumage, with black tips to the feathers, which entirely
conceal the wings and tail. The upper part of the neck and the
head are covered with sparse hair-like feathers and each foot
bears three toes of almost equal size. Emus live in parties,
pairing off for the breeding season, when the female, smaller
than the male, lays seven to thirteen eggs. Cassowaries, of which
there is only one species in Australia and the islands to the
north, have a general resemblance to the emus although differing markedly in outward appearance. The plumage is blue-
black, each wing bears five or six stout quill feathers reduced to
the bare shafts, and the head carries a horny helmet or casque.
The bare neck is decorated with brightly coloured blue and
red wattles. The toes are three in number and the inner toes
bear very long claws. Cassowaries also live in parties, pairing
off for breeding, when each hen lays three to six large green
eggs.

The moas, confined to New Zealand, became extinct within
the last 500 years, though it is impossible to determine the
exact date. They are placed in the order Dinornithiformes,
which includes several sub-families and a number of species.
The tallest moas stood twelve feet high, the smallest was about
the size of a turkey. Numerous remains of their skeletons have
been found and even some of the feathers have been preserved,
so that a good general idea of their appearance can be had. In
the form of the body they recall the emu, but the legs were much
stouter. At the same time the carriage of the body, combined
with great strength of the legs, gives them an unmistakable
resemblance to the kiwis. The size and shape of the head and
beak are, however, more in keeping with those of emus and
ostriches. The foot of the moa had four strong toes with one
directed backwards, and the feathers bore a long aftershaft as in
emus.

In former times, also, there were the several species of elephant-
birds (*Aepyornis*) of Madagascar, that survived long enough to
give rise to stories of the roc, the fabled bird said to be able to
bear young elephants away. *Aepyornis* laid an egg thirteen

inches long by nine and a half inches, with a capacity of more than four gallons, and its probable height of 10 ft. leaves no doubt that it never did fly in spite of what is said in the adventures of Sindbad the Sailor.

Finally we come to the best-known of New Zealand's animal treasures, the kiwi. Perhaps the most remarkable thing about the kiwi, or Apteryx, is that it should be so well known. E. G. Turbott, writing in *New Zealand Bird Life* describes it as a furtive night bird which is rarely seen. He tells how one may spend many days in the bush examining likely places, the hollow logs fringed with rootlets of the climbing rata, holes in the ground, in fact any inaccessible place capable of serving as a retreat, only, with luck, to see at last perhaps a single hair-like feather betraying the presence of the bird. This ability to hide is, to say the least, one of the factors contributing to continued survival. When the kiwi comes out at dusk to feed, it moves about quietly, feeling its way—so it is supposed—by means of the long bristles surrounding the base of the beak, since the eyes are very small. In appearance it recalls a large, active hedgehog as it stoops its way through the undergrowth, for the kiwi does not walk upright. Like the hedgehog, also, it is anything but silent while feeding, prodding the soft ground and rotting wood and sniffing loudly as it searches for worms, insects and grubs. The sense of smell, and those parts of the brain associated with it, are much better developed than in other birds. A kiwi's diet also includes fruits and leaves, taken more especially when the ground is dry. For defence the bird relies on speed, running with long strides of its powerful legs fast enough to leave a human pursuer behind. This gait has been described as a bounding canter, the body swaying from side to side in an ungainly manner, with no wings worthy of the name to balance it, and no tail, and with the head stretched forward to its fullest extent. But while it readily seeks refuge in running, a kiwi can, if need be, defend itself with powerful thrusts, forward and downward, of the foot, which is armed with strong claws.

Another advantage possessed by the kiwi is the efficient bill, a long slender probe with the nostrils situated near the end. It can be thrust into soft ground, enabling the bird to follow every movement of its prey.

Although little is known of the actual nesting habits, nests have been often found, in a burrow in a bank, under the hollow of a rotten log or between the roots of a tree. Each nest contains one large white egg, occasionally two; these are larger, in proportion, than those of any other bird. This is correlated with the hatching of the chick in an advanced stage of development: a ball of soft feathers which is very soon able to forage with the parents.

Although it is usual to speak of *the* kiwi, there are, in fact, five species, differing in small details of colour and size. About as big as a domestic hen, the plumage is a reddish-brown or grey marked with darker tints. As long ago as the beginning of this century, one writer described the kiwis as being on the verge of extinction, and doubtless, in spite of the protection now afforded by law, their expectation of life cannot be long. The Maoris hunted them for food, as they did the now extinct moas, but the first white settlers speeded up the work of extermination. Today, kiwis are found mainly on the higher, scrub-covered grounds. It is to be hoped, however, that the characteristic piercing whistle, *k-wee*, will be heard down the bush-covered valleys for some time yet.

Kiwis, and other relict animals of New Zealand, have been preserved largely because of their early isolation. During the early part of the Cretaceous period, there may have been a land-bridge with south-eastern Asia which would have disappeared some 80 million years ago, before the close of that period. Mammals had already come into existence, but we may presume that either they did not reach New Zealand, or that the few that did do so soon died out, except for the two species of indigenous bats; these latter, it must be remembered, however, may have flown there. Indeed, the absence of mammals suggests that New Zealand was isolated earlier than at the close of the

76. NEW ZEALAND'S BEST-KNOWN LIVING FOSSIL

Cretaceous. The first Maoris to arrive found the large flightless moas, up to twelve feet high, with which kiwis have some relationship. But mere size and speed are of less avail than secretive habits against persecution by man, and for this reason the small nocturnal bird relying on unobtrusiveness has survived the giants.

Its claims to be considered a living fossil are, however, more positive than this. The whole bony skeleton and the muscles of the kiwi suggest a terrestrial animal. This could be a secondary development, except that in many features of the skeleton, the kiwi retains as a permanent condition the same phase of development which is temporary in, say, the young chick or eaglet. The shoulder girdle, strongly developed in flying birds, is scarcely more developed than the same part in the embryos of most other birds. Again, whereas in most birds the bones are light and filled with air cells, the hollow bones of the kiwi contain marrow—also a temporary condition in the young of most birds.

Pycraft has put forward an interesting suggestion:

. . . the length of the upper arm bone or humerus, in proportion to the fore-arm, is extremely long, slender and curved. If we infer, as we may justly do, that the wing has shrunk at the same rate in all its segments, we must conclude that this was a wing with a very short hand and a very long humerus, as in, say, the Albatross, or the Rhea.

It could be, therefore, that the fore-limb of the kiwi is a degen-erate lizard-like limb rather than the modified limb of the flying birds. This is, to say the least, supporting evidence for the view, held by a minority of ornithologists, that the ancestors of kiwis never did fly. The feathers of the kiwi are loose and pendant, and the barbs do not, as in flying birds, connect with each other to form a surface resistant to the passage of air. Again, Pycraft has something to say:

> The few degenerate quill-feathers which yet remain are remarkable for the fact that the part answering to the "rhachis", which bears a small, degenerate vane, remains as hollow as the quill, and has free edges turning inwards. In birds with functional quills this rhachis is filled with a mass of pith-like cells. But this is not all. These quills, retaining the vane throughout life, are exactly similar in structure to those of the immature Cassowary, wherein . . . the vane is shed when the mature plumage is assumed and the hollow quill becomes solid.

If we were to take the testimony of the fossils, the ratites would have to be dated no earlier than the Pleistocene and Pliocene, but if we are to have a true picture this must be treated as a part only of the evidence.

There is a general impression that the kiwi is more of a relic, more truly a living fossil, than any other of the ratites; on the other hand there is quite as much to be said for regarding the emu as a living fossil too. To uphold the argument in favour of this we must know more about the moas, even although they are extinct and, therefore, do not come strictly within the scope of our discussion. There is another good reason for dealing at length with the moas, as we shall see, for no examination of the present position and relationship of the rest of the ratites can be complete without some knowledge of these birds.

Unfortunately, our knowledge of the moas leaves much to be desired in spite of the mass of bones they have left behind.

Precisely when the moas became extinct is unknown, and estimates vary very much. The usual guarded statement is that probably a few lingered on in South Island until Captain Cook visited it. The assessment made by Lindsay Buick, who has made the most complete study of moas, and has published his results in a book entitled *The Mystery of the Moa* (1931), is that the last of them lingered on until the early years of the reign of Queen Victoria.

The number of species known is subject to a similar doubt. Owen (1843) recognised seven species and placed them all in one genus. Reichenbach (1850), the German naturalist, recognised seven species belonging to seven genera. Von Haast (1873) divided them into 10 species among four genera. Lyddeker (1891) pushed the total up to 23 species belonging to five genera. Parker (1895) reduced the number to 21 species and the same five genera. Lord Rothschild, who started off with the firm conviction that previous authors had made too many species, finished up with 38 species shared among seven genera. Finally, Buick (1931) thought there were 22 or 23 species and five genera. Presumably, therefore, if we suppose that the remains of some score of species have been identified, we shall not be making a statement which lays us open to severe criticism.

Incidentally, the Maoris recognised seven kinds of moa; the great moa, the large-quilled moa, the crested moa, the hand-some moa, the double-feathered moa, the hairy moa, and the little moa. Reconstruction of moas usually takes one form only, a kind of monstrous emu, but if the Maori names have any value, even these seven kinds suggest a wide diversity of form and appearance.

It is not known for certain how many eggs any of these species laid at a time. There is the traditional statement from Maori witnesses that a female moa (species not stated) laid about thirty eggs. On the other hand, there was recovered from

Tiger Hill the skeleton of an adult moa and underneath it the skeletons of four chicks. The assumption is that these are the remains of a family overtaken by disaster, and that four was the normal number of eggs. In neither of these estimates is there any solid proof. The Maori statement may be an exaggeration, or an approximation, or it may be merely a round figure. The parent bird that died sheltering the four chicks may already have lost part of her brood previously. Here again, then, we must fall back on a cautious statement: that possibly a female moa laid four to thirty eggs at a time; and then add the rider that the number probably varied with the species.

Despite the fact that the various forms of ratites are assigned each to an order, suggesting a distant—or, at least, a not-too-close—relationship it is nevertheless the case that all writers on the subject, eminent or otherwise, persistently refer to emus as "ostrich-like birds". They do the same for the cassowaries, for the rheas and the moas, and the rest. Moreover, if one examines a series of skeletons belonging to all these birds, recent or extinct, so that the eye can wander from one skeleton to the other without interruption, no doubt is left in one's mind that —minor differences notwithstanding—they all belong to related birds, and closely related ones at that. In any case, were this not so, then the universal practice of describing them as "ostrich-like" would make still less sense. The alternative to it, which is implied in the classification, and is often even more strongly implied in the writings of most, if not all, authorities on the subject, is the vague suggestion that the various large ratites have evolved separately, the rheas in South America, the ostriches in Africa, the emus and cassowaries in Australasia, and so on. This, on the face of it, would be contrary to all we know of evolution elsewhere in the animal kingdom, and in birds in particular. But even this alternative must presuppose a common ancestor, much farther back in time, or else we must fall back on the creation of special types. There seems nothing unreasonable, therefore, in starting with the premise that rheas, ostriches, emus, cassowaries, moas (and probably others) form

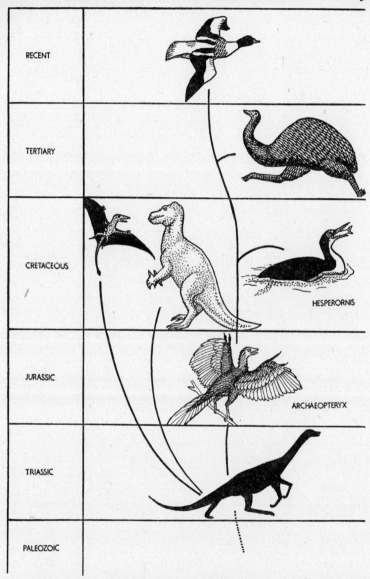

RECENT

TERTIARY

CRETACEOUS

HESPERORNIS

JURASSIC

ARCHAEOPTERYX

TRIASSIC

PALEOZOIC

77. HISTORY OF BIRDS AS USUALLY UNDERSTOOD. From a bipedal reptile arose the pterodactyls, and the bird-footed dinosaur. The third line led through Archaeopteryx (the lizard-bird) to modern birds, with the Ratites as a side-branch.

a related group springing from a common stock. The inclusion of all in a common sub-class, the Ratites, by all writers on ornithology, is a tacit admission of this, however grudgingly it may be made.

As we have already seen, as late as the early Jurassic, there is believed to have been a land-mass stretching from the present South America across Africa to Australia. A connection between Australia and New Zealand at about that time is not so certain, but there seems the likelihood that there may have been a land-bridge. We have seen in previous chapters how the former existence of a continuous land-mass from South America to Australia explains the present-day distribution of peripatus, and of the marsupials. There seems no reason why it should not also explain the present-day distribution of the ratites, especially since the large-bodied ratites, the rheas, ostriches, emus and cassowaries are if anything more closely related than are the present-day marsupials in Australia and South America, even without taking *Coenolestes* into considera-tion. If, then, these stocks were sufficiently strongly established at the time Gondwanaland began to split into its component parts, then the ratite stock must antedate the middle of the early Jurassic.

The usually accepted idea of the evolution of the bird-stock is that given in fig. 77: from a reptilian ancestor it evolved through Archaeopteryx, the famous "reptile-bird" of the Solenhofen stone, to modern birds, with the ratite stock diverg-ing at a late period, and not much before the appearance of the modern carinate birds. But Archaeopteryx was found in a rock belonging to the Upper Jurassic, so that, if the analogies argued here are correct, the ratite stock must have overrun Gondwanaland while it still stretched from South America to Australia and possibly New Zealand. That is, in the Lower Jurassic times or even earlier.

There are two more arguments in favour of this view. Archaeopteryx is known from two specimens only, from Bavaria. There obviously were more, and we can accept the statement that it must have been a lucky accident that preserved these very few specimens. On the other hand, there is no evi, dence that the Solenhofen specimens are widespread, and they could well represent a localised form. The position with the ratites is very different. There is positive evidence of their wide, spread range. The fossil record shows us not only moas in the Pleistocene of New Zealand, and related forms, such as *Dromornis* and *Genyornis* in the Pleistocene of New South Wales, but the *Aepyornis* in the Pleistocene and later strata in Madagascar. If we are to accept, as is generally stated, that the legends of the roc and the phoenix are founded on *Aepyornis*, like birds, then we have to suppose the possibility that large ratites other than ostriches—either species of *Aepyornis* or related forms—were still living in Africa and Arabia, the homes of these legends, within historic times. This should not be too remarkable, since the ostriches themselves ranged from Africa to Arabia, and fossil ostriches have been found in the Siwalki Hills of India, and in the Islands of Samoa—a fossil ostrich egg even in the Gobi desert. In Europe we have the remains of *Gasterornis*, another "ostrich-like bird" from the Lower Eocene of the basins of both London and Paris; and in the Cretaceous of Kansas, U.S.A., we have the remains of the tooth-billed *Hesperornis*, which has been labelled, whether justifiably or not, the "toothed swimming ostrich". In other words, the ratites as now represented by rheas, ostriches, emus and cassowaries, present all the signs of being an ancient and archaic race. There is the widespread distribution in geological times, certainly from the Eocene, less certainly from the Cretaceous (*Hesperornis*) and possibly from the beginning of the Jurassic or earlier. The ratite skull is admitted by all ornitholo, gists to be more primitive than the skull of carinates. And, finally, we have the attainment of giant body size, especially in *Aepyornis* and moas, seeming to tell of a race in decline.

One of the few ornithologists to make a close study of the anatomy of living ratites, the late Dr. Percy Lowe, came to the conclusion that these birds never did fly; that they were truly

flightless. His work has received little acceptance, yet his conclusions are supported by the evidence of distribution and the
biology of the ratites as a whole. In such an analysis as this,
where the available data are so scanty, even the smallest point
must assume a significance, and the following items help to
corroborate the thesis that all the living ratites are very closely
related.

We have seen early in the chapter that the kiwi lays a single
egg, rarely two. These eggs are unusually large compared with
the body of the female. Also in this chapter we saw that the
female ostrich lays up to fifteen large eggs, the rhea lays a dozen
large eggs, the emu lays seven to thirteen, and the cassowary
three to six large eggs. The four-gallon egg of the *Aepyornis*
has been mentioned, although it is not known how many this
bird laid at a time. Finally, the moas laid sufficient eggs to give
rise to the Maori tradition that they laid thirty at a time, and
even if we halve this number it is still formidable, and more
likely to be near the truth than the four based on the evidence of
the Tiger Hill skeletons, unless we suppose that over the range
of the score or so species of moa, the number varied from four
to fifteen (or even thirty). At all events, we can say that all
species show a tendency to produce a bulky volume of egg-
material at a sitting, whether in the form of the phenomenally
large egg of the kiwi or the moa's doubtful clutch of thirty.

There is another feature of ratite behaviour that should not be
too readily dismissed. We have seen that rheas live in company
with deer and guanacos, that ostriches associate with zebras and
antelopes, and, on the authority of Buick, we find that the
moas associated in flocks with the *Kara-tarepo*, the flightless
"garrulous goose", whose noisy warning cries added to difficulties of the early Maoris in hunting the moa. These things
may be pure coincidence, for many birds do tend to associate
with other animals, but they have the appearance of a "family-
trait".

Perhaps the strongest evidence for a closer relationship than
is normally assumed for the ratites comes from the evolutionary

picture of the group as a whole. To make for clarity, we will put aside the question of the kiwis for the moment. That leaves us with a score of species of moa in New Zealand, one emu in Australia, one cassowary in Australia and thirteen in the islands to the north, one ostrich in Africa and Arabia, and three species of rheas in South America. In addition, there is an unknown number of species of *Aepyornis* in Madagascar, there are various fossil remains in Australia and the northern hemisphere, and quite certainly, other undiscovered remains all over this territory. The finding of so many remains of moas is, of course, largely due to the recent extinction of these birds and to special circumstances to be discussed later. Even so, it is positive evidence of the existence of a large group of species and suggests an epicentre in the region of New Zealand with evolutionary lines radiating westwards and northwards.

A number of reptiles are known to have existed having long hind-limbs and much reduced fore-limbs. If we can imagine such a bipedal reptile, but more generalised and with the rudiments of feathers replacing the scales on its body, then we can see how the ratites may have arisen. The replacement of scales by feathers is largely hypothetical although supported by good circumstantial evidence. To understand the further necessary changes we must come to present-day studies of living animals. There are good reasons for believing that, in a given species, the behaviour of individuals on the edge of the range is slightly different from the typical. We also know that animals belonging to a single species will show marked variations in different parts of their range, where the communities making up the species are isolated. An outstanding example of this is seen in the Atlantic seals. In the past few years it has been shown that the habits of those seals inhabiting the islands off the Welsh coast are different in many respects from those of the seals living on the Scottish islands. To a lesser degree the same may be said, or suspected, of species having a discontinuous range over a continuous area of land. In fact, it seems to hold good wherever isolation of communities or groups occurs, whether this is due to the existence of actual islands, or "islands" formed between rivers, mountain ranges or other geographical barriers. Changes in behaviour could be the first steps to changes in structure.

All the potentialities for such changes may be presumed to be accumulating in an original generalised species as it spreads and extends its range. There is the likelihood, also, that as the range extends, not only will communities or parts thereof migrate, changing as they go, eventually to form new species, but that at the epicentre there will be the main proliferation of species, probably largely round its margins. We have seen such a picture built up from examination of the remains of the Camelidae, and of the horses. As further time elapses, in the case of our hypothetical stock, there will almost certainly be a dying-out at the centre. The group we are now dealing with, the ratites, is a comparatively young one, and the dying-out may be in its early stages. In fact, the extinction of the moas could represent such a process.

On Osborn's postulate of adaptive radiation, as this exten-sion of range and evolution of species was fulfilled, there should have arisen at the height of the ratite development the five types already referred to. Of these, the moas, emus, casso-waries, ostriches and rheas, and *Aepyornis*, could represent the cursorial type. Then the kiwis would stand as the modern representatives of the fossorial ratites. It is true we have to look hard for the other types. We have no evidence of climbing ratites, but then we know very little about the habits even of the moas, which died out almost before our eyes. Nobody could tell solely from the skeleton of a tree kangaroo, for example, that it habitually climbed trees. In the general proportions of the hind-limbs, however, and of the much reduced fore-legs, a tree kangaroo and a small moa are not so very different. It would only need one with less massive leg-bones and the wing-bones still present to make a climbing moa possible. For the aquatic line we can look, somewhat dubiously, to *Hesperornis*; but the greater likelihood is that we can look more profitably elsewhere.

It has been suggested that penguins are primitive and that their ancestors, like those of the ratites, never did fly. If so, they could represent an aquatic line arising from the ancestral ratite stock. Certainly this is drawing a bow at a venture, but following the law of adaptive radiation the penguins have the habits and occupy the areas where we should expect to find aquatic ratites. This leaves the volant line, but we do not necessarily have to suppose that all the modern flying birds must be descended from a stock represented by the Archaeopteryx. It, and others like it, could represent a dead-end in evolution, comparable with the trilobites, eurypterids, and a host of other groups. Some of the flying birds of the southern hemisphere could well represent the volant line derived from ratite stock, and in this connection we should recall that the hoatzin of South America is one of the most primitive birds. Unfortunately, as one writer puts it: "the story of fossil birds is far from complete"—a masterpiece of under-statement.

It is usually implied that the Maoris, who hunted the moas for their flesh, and took their eggs for food, killed off the birds before their time. That they did do these things is shown by the finding of bones and fragments of egg-shell in their kitchen middens. But it looks as if the Maoris, at most, administered the *coup de grâce*. The conclusion Buick came to at the end of his exhaustive inquiries was that the Maoris hunted only the smaller species, that the larger species were already extinct before they settled in New Zealand. This has been ascribed to various causes: volcanic eruption, earthquakes, changes of climate, disappearance of forests, endemic disease, and so on. Moa bones are found in great quantities, in swamps, in caves, in clefts in the rocks, with clear signs that the birds were driven there by lava flows, showers of hot ashes, by forest- and grass-fires. Many of the bones show signs of diseases. All these things may have contributed to the downfall of the moa, but quite obviously no single cause was responsible for killing off the whole group, since some of the species survived into the last few centuries. Probably the truth lies in the conclusions arrived at by Buick:

. . . the moa . . . lived upon the earth for some millions of years and the time was approaching when, in the natural course of events, it would have died out, just as many other primitive types had died out, having fulfilled its part in the scheme of nature. A period of decline had set in, as is evidenced by the earlier disappearance of the larger types, and this period was well on its way when man arrived upon the scene, and, by his destructive agencies, hastened and completed the exit of an already dying bird.

CHAPTER XIII

HOOFED ANIMALS IN ECLIPSE

EVEN Pedro de Cieza de Leon, a soldier and historian, with no pretensions to being a naturalist, wrote in his *Crónica del Péru*, in 1541, that the llamas were the size of donkeys, part sheep and, he added, part camel. Four centuries later we no longer doubt that llamas and camels are distant cousins; even though the first live in South America and the second in Asia, except where they have been transported elsewhere by man. The story of the relationship between these two, and the reason for their geographical separation, falls well within our series of survivals.

There are only two species of camel today: the Arabian or one-humped camel, known as a dromedary when trained for racing or riding; and the Bactrian or two-humped camel. The first is not known in the wild state and there is the likelihood that it is a domesticated form of the Bactrian, although there is no direct proof of this and even the circumstantial evidence for it rests upon the interpretation of historical relics, such as ancient writings, sculptures, pottery and so forth. There is also the slender evidence from crossing the two species, which hybridise readily, the offspring being always one-humped; or if two-humped, the hinder hump is little more than a fleshy shadow. On the other hand, there is always the possibility that the one-humped camel may be the domesticated form of a wild species that has become extinct within historical, or prehistorical times. There is no concrete evidence for this either. On the other hand, several other species of Camelidae are known only from remains associated with human settlements, showing that they have become extinct within relatively recent times. And the same could have happened to the ancestors of the one-humped camel.

Outwardly the two camels are markedly different. The fully grown Arabian camel is six and a half to seven feet at the shoulder. The Bactrian camel is larger and, in addition to having the second hump, the body carries much more hair. And yet they have much in common. Each has the two-toed feet with nails and tough padded soles, the long legs, long neck, and the complex stomach. In both, the teeth include incisors in upper and lower jaws, small canines and grinding cheek-teeth.

The llamas, as the Spanish historian rightly pointed out, are half-camels. They comprise the domesticated llama and alpaca, and the wild guanaco and vicugna. Smaller in size than the camels, all four lack the hump, have short tails and woolly coats. A more marked difference is seen in the foot, in which the two pads are separate instead of being joined, as in camels. On the other hand, they share with the camels the slit nostrils, the mobile upper lip, and the seemingly haughty and super-cilious air. They also have the complex stomach, and other internal details such as the teeth are similar to those of camels. There can be little question that they are related, and that the camels, on the one hand, and the llamas, on the other, represent end-pieces in divergent lines of evolution.

The earliest known remains of camel-like animals are found in North America, represented by the fossil *Protylopus*, from the Upper Eocene, some 50 million years old. It was about the size of a hare, and although the skull was not truly camel-like, its structure foreshadowed that of the later camels, but the teeth were more numerous. The front foot bore four toes, the middle pair being larger than the other two. The hind-foot bore two toes only, with splint bones representing the vestiges of the other two. From *Protylopus* or its congeners there appear to have sprung several lines of descent. During the Oligocene, 10 to 15 million years later, the cameloid remains had become more numerous, and it seems possible to recognise a main stem leading more or less directly to the present-day camels, and a side-shoot of giraffe-like camels which apparently died out in the Pliocene, a further 30 million years or so later. The earliest of the giraffe-like camels is *Paratylopus*, from the Oligocene, but *Oxydactylus*, from the Miocene, is better known from more numerous remains. Its body was about the size of that of a llama, its legs long and thin, and the neck long and giraffe-like. It seems to have given rise to *Alticamelus*, the remains of which are found in the late Miocene to the early Pliocene. *Alticamelus* was remarkable for its grotesquely long, thin legs and neck. It seems to have died out, leaving no descendants.

The course of the main stem of the camelids is marked by a series of skeletons found in North America, showing two main features: that they increased progressively in size and that they then went into decline, dying out, as we shall see later, within the historic period, it is thought, after sending emigrants into Asia during the Pliocene. At about the time that this emigration took place, a side branch arose—the llamas—whose history and migration we can follow down the North American continent into South America during the Pliocene and the Pleistocene.

The main stem from the hare-sized *Protylopus* of the Upper Eocene gave rise in the Oligocene to a series of genera, of which *Poebrotherium* is typical. This animal stood three feet high at the shoulder. Its skull was substantially the same as that of *Protylopus*, it still had the full complement of teeth, the legs had not developed a cannon bone, nor had the feet developed pads, so far as can be deduced from the shape and size of the toe bones. There were changes, however, to remind us that it was advancing along the road towards the camels as we know them today. Both fore- and hind-foot had now only two toes, the two middle toes which in *Protylopus* were already enlarged; the two side toes, functionally the second and the fifth digits, being reduced to tiny nodules. In addition to *Poebrotherium*, the Oligocene saw other genera, such as *Paratylopus*, *Tanupolama* and *Poebromylus*, all showing similar but slight changes. *Protomeryx*, of the Lower Miocene, showed little alteration other than a slight reduction in the size of the incisors. In the

Middle Miocene, however, *Protolabis* was marked by an increase in body size, and the upper incisors were growing smaller. In the Upper Miocene came *Procamelus*, with a skull larger than that of modern camels, but characterised by a long face and a small cranium. The legs had cannon bones; the toes had pads; and the middle incisors had been lost. *Procamelus* died out in the Lower Pliocene, and was replaced by a whole series of giant forms, *Colossocamelus*, *Megacamelus*, *Megatylopus*, *Gigantocamelus* and *Hesperocamelus*, some of which stood fifteen feet high at the shoulder with their heads some twenty feet above the ground. This was the last we find of the main stem in North America, except for *Camelops hesternus*, standing seven feet at the shoulder, the size of a well-grown camel of today. It first became known through skeletons recovered from the famous La Brea tar-pits, but from evidence obtained in 1939, in the San Joaquin Valley in California, there can be little doubt that the species persisted into recent times and that it was actually hunted by the Indians within the last thousand years. Its bones have been found, with those of the bison and other recent animals, together with stone implements, bone tools, and the ashes of camp fires. And at Fillmore, in Utah, a skull of *Camelops* was found with dried flesh still adhering to it.

In early Oligocene times, possibly earlier—although there is no certain evidence of this—camelids appeared in Asia, presumably having crossed the land-bridge that formerly joined America and Asia, across what is now the Bering Strait. The earliest remains have been named *Paracamelus*. These, found in Shansi Province and as far west as Odessa, recall strongly the camels contemporaneous with them in North America. The migration in the Oligocene did not reach much farther west than Odessa, but later, the remains of *Camelus knoblochi* have been found in European Russia and of *Camelus alutensis* in Rumania, both dating from the Holocene. The Bactrian and Arabian camels are closely related to these.

This brings us to the end of the main stem of evolution, that which ended in the modern camels, and we must return to

78. THE CAMEL'S JOURNEY: remains of early camels are found in North America. The dark line shows the probable migrations of their descendants. The dotted line represents the probable course taken by ancestors of the tapirs.

North America to follow the other line of evolution, that of the llamas. There is little to show how or when this diverged from the main stem, but that little is sufficiently convincing. In Kansas we have the remains, in the Oligocene, of *Pliauchenia*, foreshadowing the modern llamas, but larger. And whereas the present-day wild guanaco and vicugna, together with their domesticated forms, the llama proper and the alpaca, are confined to the northern Andes and the southern plains, the bones of related but extinct species are found, in the Pliocene, at other points to the west and north of South America. A more recent form than these, *Paleolama*, has been found in the prehistoric tumuli of the Argentine.

There is, therefore, clear evidence that the camelid stock, which began in North America in the Eocene, a mere 50 to 70 million years ago, rose to its zenith in the giant forms of the Pliocene, say, 10 million years ago, and that within the last 10,000 years there has been a wholesale loss of species. These included *Camelops*, and the two species of *Camelus*, *C. knob-lochi* and *C. alutensis*, and, among the llamas, various species of *Paleolama* and *Lama*. Of the two branches of the camelid stock, one became almost extinct; for, although it is now agreed that small numbers of the Bactrian camel (*Camelus bactrianus*) found today in the Gobi desert are probably truly wild, the issue was for long undecided. Certainly, but for domestication the Bactrian camel would rank as one of the rare mammals of today, even if it had not become extinct; and, as we have seen, the Arabian camel (*Camelus dromedarius*) is unknown as a wild animal. The wild llamas did not so nearly reach the verge of extinction, but there is little doubt that they too would be less well known but for the domestication of the llama and the alpaca. One thing that has contributed to the salvation of the vicugna is the quality of its silky coat. Agile and speedy, it is hunted, sheared and released again.

What justification there may be for including the camels and llamas in a dissertation on living fossils must remain a matter of opinion. Even if there were but little claim to include them under this heading, the comparison of their histories with those of other species of recent mammals would have much to con-tribute to the allied subject, that of animals in decline. For the moment, however, let us take this question of whether or not camels and llamas may be accepted as living fossils. As we have seen, one of the definitions of a living fossil is an organism that has survived beyond its era. It may, therefore, be worth quoting, both in this connection and for the further information it contains, a statement in that most authoritative work, *The Succession of Life through Geological Time*. On page 45 we read:

The Tertiary era is the Age of Mammals. During the Paleocene—the important period of transition between the Cretaceous and Eocene—mammals were rapidly obtaining dominance on the land. The most primitive mammals were small five-toed creatures with tiny brains and low-crowned teeth suitable for eating soft plants or insects. In Paleocene times these early types were evolving into a great variety of animals, with body and brains of increasing size, and teeth and limbs adapted to many different modes of life. All the main groups of placental mammals, including rodents, insectivores, primates, carnivores, ungulates (or hoofed animals), whales and sea-cows, also pouched mammals such as opossums, existed in Eocene times.

The earliest supposed remains of mammals are a few teeth belonging to a beast now named *Haramiya*, but originally called *Microlestes*, found in the late Triassic. The oldest known remains, however, are from the Jurassic, representing mammals no bigger than rats, for the most part. The date for the commencement of the Jurassic is given as 170 million years ago; the Eocene began 75 million years ago and lasted 30 million years. It would be remarkable, therefore, if mammals as a class included no forms that had become extinct, even since the Eocene, and none in decline at the present day. There have, of course, been many that have died out, both before the Eocene and since, and these need not concern us here. Rather, the insistence should be on those that, in general, we may group as "in decline".

The first example that comes to mind, and one which bears a strong resemblance to the story of the camels and llamas, is that of the tapirs. In the quotation given above, reference is made to the Ungulates or hoofed animals. In the older classification, all hoofed animals, whether odd-toed, like the horse, or even-toed (cloven-hoofed), like pigs and cattle, as well as camels, giraffes, elephants, rhinoceroses and the rest, were lumped together in a single order, the Ungulata. Today, this miscellaneous grouping is replaced by a number of orders. These are: the Proboscidea (elephants), Hyracoidea (hyraxes), Sirenia (sea-cows), Perissodactyla (horses, tapirs, rhinoceroses), and Artiodactyla (pigs, camels, cattle, giraffes, sheep, antelopes and deer).

The assumption is that the first mammals had, like the reptiles from which they are believed to have sprung, five digits on each foot. In some mammals, including man, this number is still preserved, completely or partially, but in the so-called ungulates one of the most important features is the decrease in the number of digits with the increased specialisation of the foot. This reaches its highest expression in the Perissodactyla, in the horses and their relatives, the asses and zebras, in which an enormously lengthened middle digit is all that is left, with a pair of splint/ bones to mark the degeneration of the second and fourth digits.

The tapirs, which are included in the Perissodactyla, com/ bine many of the features of the ancestral Perissodactyla. On the fore/feet the digits still number four, and there are three digits on each hind/foot; the ulna and the fibula are complete and distinct, whereas in the horse, the ulna is much reduced and fused to the radius, while the fibula bears the same relation to the tibia. The teeth of tapirs are complete; that is, they number forty/two, whereas in the horse they number thirty/six (or forty if the four canines be included, but these are normally vestigial and often absent, especially in mares). The snout of a tapir is con/ tinued into a short trunk, supported by shortened and arched nasal bones, a feature which is seen too in rhinoceroses, also members of the Perissodactyla showing many primitive features.

The tapirs include one genus only, *Tapirus*, with a discon/ tinuous distribution similar to that of the camels and llamas. The Malayan tapir (*T. indicus*) ranges from Tenasserim and southern Siam in the north, to Sumatra and possibly Borneo in the south. It is seldom seen, for in the evergreen jungles where it lives its shyness and preference for dense cover and for the water keeps it well out of sight. In addition, its flesh is not in demand and it carries no trophies to tempt the sportsman. It is, indeed, this ability to keep out of sight that makes it uncertain whether the tapir does inhabit Borneo, but there have been several reports, so far unconfirmed, of its having been seen there.

The South American tapirs resemble the Malayan species in that they are stoutly built, about the size of a donkey, and have the same secretive habits. But whereas in the Malayan species the fore/parts and limbs are black and the rest of the body white, the South American species are entirely blackish/ brown. Of the several species, the lowland form (*Tapirus terrestris*) is the most common, inhabiting the Brazilian forests.

The mountain tapir (*T. roulinii*), living in the Andes of Colombia, Ecuador and Peru, up to heights of 14,000 feet, is somewhat scarce and very little is known about it. The chief enemy of the South American species is the jaguar, and of the Malayan species, the tiger; with the absence of molestation from man, the only fear for the species lies in the destruction of their habitat, and this applies more especially to the Malayan area, where commercial plantations tend to replace the natural forest.

The fossil history of the tapir begins, perhaps, with the Eocene form known as *Homogalax*, which had much in common with the earliest ancestor of the horse, *Hyracotherium*, or Eohippus. By the Oligocene, 40 million years or so ago, tapirs differing little from the presentday species were in existence and from the Miocene, 20 million years ago, we have fossils almost exactly similar to the tapirs of today. The tapir may, therefore, be accepted as a fair representation of the early ancestors of the perissodactyls as a whole, widespread during the Miocene, now restricted to two widely separated areas of the world, having followed very much the path of the camels and llamas. It is as much a living fossil as tuatara, although its lineage may not cover so wide a span of time.

The Equidae, the second family of living Perissodactyla, has a similar history, although its outlines are apt to be masked by the abundance of the domesticated horses and asses, and by the formerly numerous zebras. The history of the horse is so well documented in the fossil record, and has been so fully recorded by Dr. G. G. Simpson in *Horses*, that the barest summary need be given here. The story begins with Eohippus, a name which, by the laws of zoological nomenclature must be displaced by *Hyracotherium*. Simpson wisely proposes to retain such a wellknown name by using it as a common name. Eohippus, at its maximum about the size of a mediumsized dog, was common in Europe and North America at the beginning of the Eocene. There were a number of species of *Hyracotherium*, those in Europe dying out, so that the development of the horse stock took place in North America. There, during the subsequent 70 million years or so, were developed *Mesohippus*, in the Oligocene, *Merychippus*, in the Miocene, and *Pliohippus* in the Pliocene. Finally, in the Pleistocene we have the appearance of the genus *Equus* itself, in very much its present form. During this development there occurred a gradual increase in body size, changes in the teeth, and the lengthening of the legs with the successive loss of the toes until there remained only the middle, much-strengthened toe forming the functional foot. Throughout this time, from the Eocene to the Pleistocene, many other forms arose, to die out after a compara-tively short while. And from time to time during the Miocene and Pliocene there were migrations from the stem-stock into the Old World (Europe and Asia), but each of these in turn died out. The maximum period in the fortune of the horses was therefore during the Miocene-Pliocene.

In the late Pliocene and Pleistocene, the genus *Equus* shows a migration similar to that of the camels and llamas. There was the movement south through the Isthmus of Panama into South America, this branch fading out in the Holocene. There was also the migration over the land-bridge across what is now the Bering Strait into Asia. Thereafter, the history of the horse becomes obscure. Within historical times, we know that with the discovery of the American continent by Europeans came its reintroduction into a land where its representatives had by then died out. And in the Old World, where the horse had become such a universal beast of burden, particularly in Europe, the wild ancestor was in eclipse.

The only true wild horse surviving today is the Mongolian Wild Horse, or Przewalski's Horse (*Equus caballus przewalskii*). This stands four and a half feet at the shoulder, is an isabelline brown with a blackish mane and a long-haired black tail. The mane is stiff and erect, and there is no forelock. Stocky in build and pony-like in appearance, its summer coat shows a dark stripe down the middle of the back and an inconspicuous shoulder stripe. On the lower parts of the legs there are usually distinct bars, extending up to the knees. Przewalski's Horse is

79. EARLY ANCESTORS OF THE HORSE. From top left down: Eohippus, *Mesohippus, Merychippus, Pliohippus, Equus.*

now on the verge of extinction, partly through being hunted for its meat by the Mongols, and partly through dilution by breeding with their domestic ponies.

There were probably other species of wild horses in Asia and in Europe. It is also probable that the domestic horse (*Equus caballus*) had its remote origins in several of them. Within historic times there existed in eastern Europe a wild horse known as the tarpan. It was small, ash-dun, with a short erect mane. It did not survive the nineteenth century and there are few accurate records of it, apart from one drawing, believed to be that of the wild living animal. Whether the tarpan contributed anything to the origin of the domesticated horse is unknown, but there is reason to believe that it interbred freely with domestic and feral horses. With the tarpan gone and Przewalski's Horse extinct or nearly so, *Equus caballus*, as a wild animal is, therefore, to all intents and purposes, extinct.

The wild asses are close relatives of the horse. How close may be gauged from the fact that some authors refer both asses and horses to the genus *Equus*, others place the asses in a subgenus *Asinus*, while yet others place the Asiatic wild asses in the genus *Equus* and the African species in *Asinus*. At all events, wild asses, standing three to four feet at the shoulder, have a short erect mane, large ears and a tufted tail. The coat is a sandy-fawn in colour, with a dark stripe down the back, usually a shoulder stripe and sometimes bars on the lower legs. The Asiatic wild asses formerly ranged from Syria and Arabia, where they are now extinct, through to central and southern Asia. There are found the various sub-species of *Equus* (*Asinus*) *hemionus*: the onager of Persia, the Indian wild ass or ghorkar of the deserts of Cutch, the kiang of Tibet and the kulan or chigetai of Transcaspia and Mongolia. Everywhere they have suffered from modern firearms, being hunted for their meat and hides, their foals ridden down for sale as domestic animals.

The African wild asses once roamed the whole of north and north-east Africa; but today, although the domesticated donkey is commonly seen, its wild relatives are almost as much in eclipse as the Asiatic wild asses. The Algerian wild ass became extinct in Roman times and although the Nubian wild ass is still present in fair numbers in the region between the Upper Nile, Abyssinia and the Red Sea, it is hunted whenever possible for its flesh. Wary and speedy, it was formerly difficult to approach, but with modern firearms and automobiles with which to hunt it, these natural advantages are of little avail. Wild asses are said to be abundant in certain parts of Somali-land, but the reports of wild asses in the Sahara probably have reference to feral donkeys. There is considerable uncertainty as to the identity of the particular wild ass from which the domesti-cated donkey has derived. Some authorities suspect it may have been from a sub-species now extinct.

Little need be said about the African striped horses, the zebras, formerly present in such vast numbers throughout the southern half of the African continent, and now severely reduced in numbers. Some of their sub-species, such as the quagga and Burchell's zebra are already extinct, and the rest survive largely under protection. The main causes of this diminution must be attributed to man's predatory (and insatiable?) habits, and the changes he has wrought in the zebra's habitat.

The story of the horse, and, indeed, of the family Equidae, could not be more aptly put than when, in 1939, C. G. Trew entitled a book on the history of the horse, *From "Dawn" to "Eclipse"*: a delightful pun expressing the sad truth about the genus *Equus*.

There is one thought which naturally obtrudes itself at this point. We have seen how the body size in the main stem of the camels increased and then decreased as the stock went into decline. This is not to say that at the height of its fortunes all species then extant were of large size. It must be emphasised that large body size refers to the larger species, and does not mean that at that time every species then living was of large size. The same is true of the Age of Giant Reptiles, and, indeed, of all such maxima in development.

To resume, then, this increase in size preceding a decline seems to partake almost of a law. It is seen again in elephants. The earliest elephant, *Moeritherium*, of the Lower Oligocene, was two feet high. The record for the present-day African elephant, the larger of the living species, is eleven feet five and a half inches, but the largest extinct elephant stood a foot higher than this, and a foot more in height means much more in bulk. Of the 350 species of elephants recognised by Osborn, who made a life's study of them, only the two are left today. Elephants, then, have passed their zenith, and their decline is marked by a reduction in body size. The same trend is seen in the sea-cows (see Chapter 14).

The rhinoceroses may be said to have begun with *Hyrachyus*, of the Eocene, a very small animal, and to have reached their peak during the Miocene-Pliocene, through forms like *Baluchitherium*, standing eighteen feet high. Today, we have five species of rhinoceros, the largest, the Great Indian rhinoceros, standing a mere six and a half feet at the shoulders. Of this species, the most we can say is that, although formerly widespread, a few only survive today in the deep jungles of Nepal, northern Bengal and Assam, and even with the official protection afforded it, there is little chance of their surviving much longer. The Javan rhinoceros, once numerous from Bengal to Sumatra, is on the verge of extinction. An estimate, made in 1937, throughout its range, gave the total of living animals as sixty-six. The Sumatran rhinoceros, although more numerous than the Javan, is everywhere decreasing in numbers. The case of the African species, the black and the white rhinoceros, is little better.

Other ungulates tell the same story. In the Oligocene there were pigs five feet high and twelve feet long. Hippopotamuses, of which there are a number of species in the Pleistocene, or sub-fossil, in Asia, Europe and Africa, are today represented by two species, the common hippopotamus and the pygmy hippopotamus, both confined to Africa. The first of these ranged within historic times from the Nile delta to the Cape but now survives in an area bounded roughly by Khartoum in the north and the Zambesi River in the south, as well as in a few protected areas of South Africa. The pygmy hippopotamus is restricted to Liberia, Sierra Leone and Nigeria.

Much of the reduction in the numbers of these beasts can be laid at the door of the human race, who slaughtered them for food, for sport and other reasons. It would, therefore, be difficult to prove that their decline is not wholly due to man's persecution of them, especially of those coming within the category of Big Game which, during the latter part of the nineteenth and the early years of the twentieth century were present in such incredible numbers in Africa. Nevertheless, there is more than a suspicion that many of these—certainly those specifically mentioned here—were, in fact, already in decline. This generalisation belongs, however, very much to the realm of conjecture, for even if each case is considered strictly on its merits, the relevant data are so inadequate that it must remain very much a matter of opinion whether the rhinoceroses, and others, are in a natural decline or one induced by man's interference. For example, in spite of what has already been said about the decline of the genus *Equus* in the Holocene, the converse could equally be argued, as we shall see.

The line of argument, that the genus *Equus* was, in fact, on the threshold of a period of prosperity, would run as follows. If we take the history of the genus in the Old World alone, since the migration in the Pleistocene, across what is now the Bering Strait, we find that horses ranged over the whole of Asia, except possibly northern Siberia, reaching the extreme south-east corner of Asia, and Arabia in the south-west. It appears that they were absent from Scandinavia and the northern parts of Europe and Asia. The wild asses inhabited a good deal of central Asia, as well as the south, and south-west, together with northern and north-eastern Africa and a part of East Africa. The zebras covered a large part of the southern half of the African continent. In other words, apart from Australasia and Malaysia, the tropical forests of Africa, Arabia and the far

16

north, the members of the horse family had colonised the whole
of the Old World. We can imagine also, that in prehistoric
times, their populations throughout this vast area must have
been countless.

As we have seen, little is known of the wild horses of Asia
and Europe. There is Przewalski's Horse (*Equus caballus
przewalskii*) and the tarpan, of which nobody knows sufficient
to give it more than the general appellation *Equus caballus*. [The
reason for repeating these names here is to make the point that
there is no suggestion of these two horses being more than sub-
species.] Further than this, we meet, in books on the subject,
the vague suggestion that there may have been other species of
wild horses that died out in the prehistoric period. If, however,
we turn to the wild asses of Asia, we find that the latest pronouncement on their classification (Ellerman and Morrison-
Scott, *Checklist of Palaearctic and Indian Mammals*) gives the
following names for the Chigetai, Onager, Ghorkhar and
Kiang respectively: *Equus hemionus hemionus*, *E. hemionus onager*,
E. hemionus khur and *E. hemionus kiang*. In addition, they list
E. hemionus hemippus, of Syria and districts around, "possibly
now extinct". The Asiatic wild asses represent, therefore, five
sub-species. There is no such recent pronouncement on the
status of the various African wild asses, but there is little doubt
that they would be grouped as sub-species of a single species,
Equus asinus. Moreover, the two species *E. asinus* and *E.
hemionus* would be admittedly very closely related.

We have seen that Przewalski's Horse has a dark stripe along
the mid-line of the back and also a shoulder stripe; and that in
the summer coat the legs are often banded below the knee.
These markings are closely similar to those found in the various
wild asses. Among the zebras, the quagga and Burchell's
zebra (*Equus quagga burchelli*) are extinct, and the remaining
zebras may be listed as follows: Grevy's zebra (*E. grevyi*), the
bontequagga of which Boehm's zebra (*E. quagga boehmi*) is the
best known, and the common zebra of South Africa (*Equus
zebra*). Again, there is the suggestion of a few closely related

species divided into sub-species. Moreover, from the most southerly form of *E. quagga*, that is, the extinct quagga—which had stripes on the fore-parts of the body only, although occasional individuals had the whole body striped—to Boehm's zebra, in Kenya, the most northerly, with the body and legs completely striped, there are, or were, all gradations.

One of the criteria of well-established species is that their characters are strongly marked, as compared with their nearest relatives. Where there is a multiplicity of sub-species or races, we may suspect that these sub-species are not of long standing, or even that they are in a state of active evolution, or speciation, as it is called. We can never have proof one way or the other so far as the genus *Equus* is concerned, for man has dealt so drastically with it that he has, in effect, smothered the evidence. On the other hand, since the genus appears to date from the end of the Pliocene at the earliest, the generic age cannot be much over a million years—not much more than that of the genus *Homo*, a very late comer on the evolutionary scene. With this suggestion that the genus *Equus* is, despite other appearances to the contrary, a young and expanding genus, may be coupled the absence of any evidence that the main stem of the Equidae had reached the maximal size and was beginning to show a diminution.

Perhaps the main feature of the history of the Equidae is the appearance of two peaks suggesting a rise followed by a decline, which in turn was followed by a resurgence. It is now suspected that this may have happened in a few other instances, but evidence is hard to obtain. If it were so, then the apparent contradiction in the case of the Equidae, exposed at some length in these pages, could be interpreted as follows: that the Equidae of the Holocene were, in fact, in decline from a second peak of development, but that this was accompanied by an incipient speciation. In other words, the family as a whole was having a last vigorous fling after being given a second chance. It looks very like the apparent juvenescence which comes to some individuals in late middle age.

CHAPTER XIV

CAUSES OF EXTINCTION

A FEW species of animals have become totally extinct within historical times, and the demise of some of them is more or less well documented. No two of these were lost for the same reasons, and the analysis of each in turn may yield some information on the causes of extinction. We can do worse than start with a story that has been told many times in recent years, yet is sufficiently illuminating to bear repetition: the story of the passenger pigeon. Native to North America, this pigeon was long-winged, coloured bluish and fawn with a slate-blue head and purplish-brown breast. At the time of the white settlement of North America, it existed in uncountable numbers. So it continued until 1866, but by 1907 it was extinct in the wild, although a few birds lingered on in the Cincinatti Zoo until 1914, when the last of its race died at 5 p.m. on September 1st. It is noteworthy also as the only species of which the exact moment of extinction is known.

Josselyn, writing in 1672 of the passenger pigeon, said: "I have seen a flight of pigeons that to my thinking had neither beginning nor ending, length nor breadth, and so thick I could not see the sun." Audubon records a flight of them continuing for three days without a break, and for three hours out of those three days he estimated that a billion passed overhead. Ross King, in 1866, saw a flock which obscured the sun for fourteen hours and was 300 miles long and one mile wide. To emphasise the enormous numbers of the pigeons, we may quote Alexander Wilson as typical of the many recorded observations. He estimated that a flock seen by him in 1832, near Frankfort, in Kentucky, numbered

2,230,270,000 birds. When, in 1857, a Bill was proposed to protect the pigeon, a committee of the Ohio State Legislature reported: "The Passenger Pigeon needs no protection. Wonderfully prolific—no ordinary destruction can lessen them." What, then, brought about its complete extermination?

As the towns grew, there was opened up a ready market for the dead birds. Their slaughter was made the more easy by the pigeon's habits. Moving in vast, densely packed flocks, even the indifferent marksman could bring down twenty or thirty with one pull of the trigger. Using small swivel-cannon, 200 could be assured at one discharge. The birds could be clubbed or netted with the greatest ease; 3,000 at one time has been recorded in a sweep of the net. There was, however, an even easier method of getting them—by cutting down the trees, especially when the young squabs were about. Worse still, it became the practice so to fell a tree that it brought down others with it. The climax in this almost frenzied attack was reached at Petosky, in Michigan, in 1878, when 300 tons of the birds were slaughtered in a few weeks. By 1895 the killing for market was finished.

This, in brief outline, is the story of the passenger pigeon, and it is usual to ascribe the bird's extermination wholly to the almost hysterical slaughter for food. The history of other exterminations teaches us that it is rare for a single factor to bring about the end of a species. The general pattern is, rather, of a concatenation of adverse circumstances, in which one only serves as the *coup de grâce*. This is almost axiomatic, so that it is worth while to examine the story of the passenger pigeon from an unorthodox angle to see how far it accords, not with the usually accepted explanation but with probable facts.

First, we have the fantastic figures for the numbers of the pigeon which, on the face of it, should have offset even such massacres as that at Petosky. Secondly, there is the brief span of time in which extermination was accomplished. It is difficult to set precise limits to this period, but we have three dates: 1857, the refusal of the Ohio State Legislature to protect the bird because of its vast numbers; 1895, when killing on an organised scale for market was finished; and 1907, when the last bird was seen in the wild. This gives us fifty years from the time of enormous abundance to complete extermination. When we remember the efforts made in Australia over a longer period, by all manner of devices, to kill off the rabbit, the tremendous and sustained efforts in various countries to eliminate rats, and other examples of this kind, which have left the quarry in virtually undiminished numbers—then, clearly, mere organised slaughter does not alone account for the loss of this one species of pigeon. Moreover, there is a period of twelve years, from the time when killing for market was finished to final extermination in the wild, in which one might reasonably have expected a recovery, instead of a steady decline.

The first obvious factor in the death of the species was the advent of a new predator, with efficient methods of killing. The second was that each pair of birds produced only one young at a time. While this slow rate of reproduction was sufficient to maintain the numbers of the population despite the attacks from predatory mammals and raptorial birds, it was inadequate in the face of an additional predator. Having said this much, we must enter the realm of conjecture.

The pigeon nested in trees and fed on beechnuts, acorns, chestnuts and the like, on raspberries, wild cherries and other fruits, even on caterpillars and other insects. In other words, for the most part it was dependent upon trees for shelter and food. Trees were felled, as we have seen, as a means of slaughtering the bird itself, but also, increasingly, with the advance of human settlement. The reduction in the number of the trees could, therefore, have been a contributory, even if minor, adverse circumstance.

Then, we learn from contemporary records that the cock and hen of a breeding pair shared the duties of incubation with a clocklike regularity. Twice a day the changeover at the nest took place, simultaneously, so far as can be gleaned, throughout the flock. And each time it occurred, the noise of the wings of the fluttering millions sounded "like a roaring tornado". Another curiosity of their behaviour was that during the breeding season, linked with the regular change-over, at any given moment of the day either all the males would be foraging and the females sitting or vice versa. This, with the contemporary accounts of the serried ranks of the migrating birds, suggests a regularity and fixity of habits. Or, conversely, a lack of elasticity in behaviour, making them more vulnerable to attack by the same methods on the same ground.

It is a marked feature of the behaviour of gregarious animals that, in order to carry out successfully the more essential actions of living, a mass stimulus is needed. This applies more especially to the breeding habits. It is not possible at this date to know much of the detailed reactions of the passenger pigeon, but it is a fair guess that its breeding, feeding and migratory habits were running in a very narrow groove; they depended upon the stimulus from massed numbers and were sufficiently fixed and regular for any disturbance, such as might result from persecution, to throw the lives of the birds completely out of gear. In other words, it is reasonable to assume that it was a species that would be bound to disappear before the advance of human settlement.

We may presume the causes of the extinction of the passenger pigeon to be manifold and capable of the following summarisation. There was a specialisation of habit and of habitat, an absence of adaptability of the bird to changing circumstances, the appearance of a new predator and a low rate of multiplication to make good the abnormal losses occasioned by this predator, coupled perhaps with a diminution in the food supply. Further than this we cannot go, but this summary underlines a cardinal feature of the causes of extinction of an animal species: that the causes are seldom single.

The heath hen, also of North America, presents us with something of a parallel to the passenger pigeon. In this instance the factors are known. Formerly abundant in the central and southern New England states, the numbers of the heath hen had been reduced by killing for the table and by the cultivation of the land. By 1870 nothing more was left than a small colony on the island of Martha's Vineyard. Twenty years later their numbers were down to 200. A successful public appeal for subscriptions to protect the survivors resulted in a tenfold increase in their numbers. Then came a series of disasters. First, there was an unusually severe winter. Then came a widespread fire at nesting-time, and, because it was their habit to sit tight on the nest, many perished. This was followed by a plague of goshawks, and finally disease broke out. By 1931 the heath hen was extinct.

Although the exploitation and settlement of the land-masses, especially by the white races, has reduced many species to a low ebb, there are comparatively few instances of species having been actually exterminated. And in none of the others is there as much material for analysis as in the two examples quoted already. Within the limits of recorded history we have lost, in addition to the two birds just described, the quagga, Burchell's zebra, the tarpan, aurochs, Steller's sea-cow, the dodo, the great auk and the moa. In the case of two of these there is reason to suppose that the species was already in decline and that human persecution did no more than finish them off. Others, such as the notornis and the cahow, believed to be extinct, have been found subsequently to exist still in small numbers in out-of-the-way places. Then we have those species such as the sea-otter and the northern sea-elephant, brought almost to vanishing point by human persecution, which have, under subsequent protection, revived and are again in a firm position. A much larger number of species have been rendered extinct locally, or have suffered severe reductions in their total populations throughout their range, but without necessarily suffering a total eclipse. In other words, it is for the most part difficult to exterminate a species, even with the use of firearms and other civilised methods of destruction, without some contribution from natural circumstances.

The great auk became extinct in 1844. It was a large

80. THE GREAT AUK: already in decline, its departure
was hastened by human persecution.

penguin-like bird, flightless, with small wings, black with a
white front and a white spot on either side of the head. This
last feature was responsible for its Gaelic name, An Gearra-
bhul, "the strong stout bird with the spot", later corrupted to
garefowl. It was also known as the pinwing, or pinion-winged
bird, whence the name penguin was derived which was later
transferred to the Antarctic birds. During the sixteenth and
seventeenth centuries, the great auk was extensively slaughtered.
Expeditions to the Newfoundland coasts, more particularly,
killed and salted down large quantities for the European
markets. Around southern Iceland, the Faroes, St. Kilda and
the Orkneys, they were also killed for food and for bait. Being
flightless they were particularly vulnerable when on their

breeding grounds. In spite of this, there must have come a time when their numbers were still considerable while not sufficient to make their commercial killing profitable; and the survivors should have been adequate to ensure the continuance of the species.

While it is usual to lay all the blame for the disappearance of the great auk on the collector and the hunter, there is some evidence that human activities were no more than a contri-butory cause. For example, in prehistoric times the bird had an even wider distribution than that indicated in the preceding paragraph for the sixteenth and seventeenth centuries. Accord-ing to J. D. Macdonald (*Illustrated London News*, January 11, 1947):

> A map of its chronological distribution forms an almost ideal picture of shrinkage. Species are distinct biological units. We should think of them as finite entities: they have an end as well as a beginning, and usually a long extended life history in which, as in individuals, can be found the various stages of growth from adaptable and lusty youth to decrepit old age. The Garefowl had its heyday in prehistoric times: its declining years were no more than shortened by human influences: the end came in 1844 when the last specimen was recorded on the island of Eldey, off Southern Iceland.

There is another example of extinction of a species which, in my opinion, is due to a natural decline and not to the rapacity of man, as is usually assumed. It concerns Steller's sea-cow. In 1741 the Danish navigator Bering and the German naturalist Steller were shipwrecked on an island off Kamchatka, later to be known as Bering Island. There Steller found a previously unknown animal, later to become famous as Steller's sea-cow. A smaller colony was found around the neighbouring Copper Island. Fully grown, the animal reached twenty-four feet in length and bore a close resemblance to the dugongs and manatees of tropical waters. The head was very small compared to the barrel-shaped body, which was dark brown, sometimes streaked or spotted with white. The

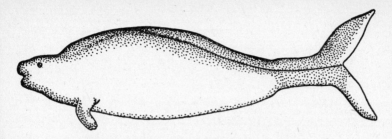

81. STELLER'S SEA-COW: drawn after the only known representation. But for human persecution this sea-cow might still be with us, a living fossil nearing its end.

fore-limbs were flippers, covered with short stiff hairs. The hind-limbs were gone and the body ended behind in a stout tail bearing at its extremity a pair of horizontal flukes. The animal differed, in fact, in no substantial respect from the tropical sea-cows, or Sirenia, that are believed to have given rise to the stories of mermaids. Its skeleton is well known, from many specimens in museums all over the world, but nothing is known of its anatomy. As to its habits, all we know is from the writings of the mid-eighteenth century writers, including Steller himself; for, by 1768, it was extinct.

Soon after the discovery of the sea-cow, the islands were visited by Russian hunters and traders, who found in this creature a welcome source of fresh meat. The animal was slow, inactive, inoffensive and without any means of defending itself. It was tied to the inshore waters, where it fed on the beds of the 100-foot-long oarweed. In other words, it was a sitting target to an experienced hunter armed with an iron-shod pole. Another characteristic that worked to its disadvantage was the habit of going to the assistance of its fellows that were wounded or otherwise in distress. Not only did this willing lamb-to-the-slaughter supply fresh meat, but stores of it were laid in for long voyages, and the island was frequently visited expressly for this purpose. Sometimes the wounded escaped or a carcase sank before it could be retrieved, so the slaughter was wasteful as well as merciless. A later writer described the extermination of Steller's sea-cow as being "simply due to man's greed", a condemnation that has been generally accepted.

It seems highly probable, nevertheless, that the species was already in decline. Although early reports spoke of the animal being there in abundance, Stejneger, writing in 1887, after visiting Bering Island to collect skeletons and such evidence as he could, suggested that to put the original population in 1741 at 1,500 is probably to over-estimate it. That of Copper Island was probably smaller. He also found evidence that numbers were not increasing, that the number of births did not equal the deaths from natural causes. Ice is very liable to form around the shores of these islands in winter, which would make some of the oarweed inaccessible to the animals. There is also the suggestion that the species did not, in fact, become extinct by 1768; that when the number became reduced to the point where catching them was difficult, the hunters no longer called at the islands. On the authority of the Russian naturalist Dybowski there is some evidence that they may have survived until at least 1830. Over and above this, it would not be unreasonable to suppose that those two islands did not represent the full extent of the range of Steller's sea-cow and that during some period prior to 1741 the range and numbers of the species had dwindled considerably, and that their ultimate extinction was only a matter of time whatever was done either to persecute or to protect.

The living relatives of Steller's sea-cow are the dugongs of the Australian seas and the Indian Ocean and the manatees of West Africa and the American coasts from Florida to the Amazon. The largest of these is not more than eight feet long, and there is no reason to suppose, from the admittedly meagre accounts available, that in any part of their range the tropical sea-cows are densely crowded in their habitat. By comparison, we have the spectacle of Steller's sea-cow requiring to feed an enormous bulk of body, restricted to a small area of inhospitable coast, with the possibility of even more limited supplies of food under exceptional weather conditions.

We have no factual evidence to go on, and conjecture can be our only guide in this. Whatever may have been the events that led up to these two colonies finding themselves occupying the inshore waters of Bering and Copper Islands respectively, there seems to be little doubt that they were well off the beat typically inhabited by members of their order. Their apparent gigantism also looks suspiciously like the increase in body size that precedes a decline in a main stem. The possibility, on Stejneger's testimony, that births did not keep pace with deaths suggests one of two things: either a shortage of food or a disadvantageous change in the psychology of the animal. The first of these is a well-known cause of a low birth-rate in animals otherwise flourishing. A psychological change may bring about a reduction in the emotional stimulus to pair. Or it could be that there was a change in the mental pattern causing the animals to be over-gregarious. As to this, we have the testimony provided by contemporary writers, of the animals crowding to an injured comrade. In human beings we should call this an excess of compassion; or, if we take the cynical view, we might say that it compares closely with people crowding round somebody injured in the street. In animals faced with a ruthless predator it is asking for trouble. The possibility of some adverse change in the specific behaviour pattern is also suggested by the fact—if Dybowski's statements are correct—that even when left alone the species failed to make good its numbers, as some other species have done. Altogether, therefore, we seem to be in the presence of a species-senility, and in this connection Macdonald's words quoted on page 236 are worth recalling.

Is it, perhaps, that gregarious species generally wilt more readily under persecution, and that this is the secret of the ready decline of the Equidae also? And if so, could we also postulate that a thinning of the ranks due to natural causes more readily affects the gregarious species, as compared with those leading a solitary life, such as tuatara, the monotremes, silverfish and others? At least, these are questions that merit further considera-tion, and to which attention could be profitably directed in future studies.

Another point arises naturally here. Reference has been made to the attainment of large size preceding a decline. It has often been asserted, dogmatically, that the giant reptiles, the dinosaurs, went down before the attacks of the more nimble-witted mammals that came on to the scene. Such an assumption may be correct but there are several arguments against it. Let us quote once again from *The Succession of Life through Geological Time*. On page 41, we read:

> The dinosaurs continued to dominate life on land. *Tyrannosaurus*, the greatest of the flesh-eating types, when standing was nearly 20 feet high. Its total length was, however, nearly 40 feet: it had fangs 6 inches long, and powerful claws for holding down its prey ... There were many kinds of plant-eating dinosaurs.

These remarks refer to the Cretaceous period. And on page 42 it says: "Mammals remained inconspicuous throughout Cretaceons times."

Further on (page 45), dealing with the Eocene, we read:

> The dinosaurs and other great reptiles which dominated the world in the Cretaceous period had now become extinct ... all the Eocene carnivores (creodonts) were primitive and small-brained ... [and] ... lived a more solitary existence than the herbivores [i.e. mainly the Eocene ungulates] on which they preyed.

Apart from the fact that the giant reptiles included both herbivores and carnivores—and one would have supposed that fearsome creatures like the *Tyrannosaurus* would have been as predaceous on, and as formidable to a giant herbivore as a

82. GIANTS OF THE PAST: examples of animals in decline beside their giant ancestors. Extinct giants (outline) and living relatives (black); Ground sloth and two-toed sloth; Pliocene tortoise and Aldabra tortoise: *Glyptodon* and giant armadillo; Upnor and African elephants; Creta-ceous and modern Crocodiles.

small, if nimble-witted, mammal—there is no suggestion in these quotations that the giant reptiles "went down" before the more active mammals.

One of the lessons we are learning—all too slowly—today is that in a stable ecology the predator is essential to its prey; speaking, that is, in terms of species rather than individuals. To begin with, no predator—excepting perhaps certain internal parasites—kills off its prey and thereby robs itself of its means of livelihood. Rather, the predator kills off the sick and the weakly, and, as a consequence, not only improves the stock generally but keeps the population more or less at a constant level. Where man has interfered and killed off, or seriously reduced, the beasts and birds of prey, one of two things has happened. Where this has been done under natural or nearly natural conditions, there has been a marked reduction in the numbers of the creatures preyed upon. The first result of protecting the prey from its natural predator is an increase in the numbers of the prey. These rise to saturation point, whereupon disease breaks out to decimate the ranks. Under conditions of cultivation, where an unnatural amount of food is available, killing off the predators converts the prey into a pest to crops. In India, pigs and monkeys have become a pest to agriculture wherever the leopard is killed off. The coyote in North America, once mercilessly persecuted, is now seen as a friend of the farmer, provided its numbers do not increase unduly. Nearer home, the best opinion now sees the killing of the predators such as stoats and hawks as a fatal mistake in game preserving, thus letting the rat have full play. These are but a few examples.

In exceptional cases only does the predator bring about the extinction of a species, and the best examples are found where man has been, wittingly or unwittingly, the agent. We may point to the extermination of the dodo, when man introduced pigs, cats and dogs to Mauritius. Here, in a limited space—an oceanic island—a highly specialised species of flightless bird "went down" before the sudden onslaught of several unnatural enemies, including, of course, man himself. We have the same story, several times repeated, of the extermination of species of small mammals where the black or brown rat is introduced to an island. Usually it is a species of rodents endemic on the island that is ousted and the cause is believed to be competition for food rather than actual attack; thus, it most frequently happens within a limited territory where there is no chance for the victim to migrate.

There may, indeed, have been instances in the geological past in which the appearance of a new predator, either by evolution or by migration from another region, has brought about the demise of a species, or even a group of species. But there is little evidence for this. Coming to modern times, there is no reason to believe that the large, sluggish-brained crocodiles have been adversely affected by the present-day nimble-witted carnivorous mammals, of which there were plenty in tropical regions—until the invention of modern firearms.

The mention of crocodiles brings us back to the point about large size heralding a decline, and we recall that there are remains of Cretaceous crocodiles forty feet long, but if croco-diles can be said to be in decline today, it can only be remarked that they are taking a very long time to die. Crocodiles, alligators and caimans are still numerous, perhaps not as to species, but certainly in numbers of populations—or would be but for man's interference. Possibly they can be construed as a dying race, another relic, and, in a sense, a living fossil, from the Age of Reptiles. If so, then we must take this as another example of the truth that species, families and orders, like individuals, do not necessarily all have the same life span.

It could be, of course, that modern crocodiles would have enjoyed a resurgence but for the advent of man's dominance of the world. This would be very difficult to argue. We cannot be sure that all species of crocodiles that lived in the past are known; and we have no hope of assessing the numbers of their populations relatively to the populations of present-day crocodiles. Indeed, we should be unable to estimate even approximately the number of crocodiles living in the world today. Precise statistical study is therefore impossible. The same is true for all animals which have lived in the past, and for most of those living today. Whether any species, genus or family has shown in its history a double peak is an extremely difficult question to answer. There are, however, a few instances in which it is suspected that a group of animals, either species, genus or family, has reached a zenith, then declined, and at a later stage in its geological history has enjoyed a recrudescence. The complete history of the horse suggests that it may sometimes happen. At all events, this is another factor which may need to be borne in mind in assessing the causes leading to survival beyond the typical epoch.

CHAPTER XV

POSSIBLE CAUSES UNDERLYING
SURVIVAL

I T is axiomatic that there are two sides to every question. Biological problems are no exception to this. We may go further and say that for most biological problems there may be several explanations equally plausible, equally feasible and equally contradictory. This can happen not merely where the evidence is scanty, but where as in the fluctuations in the numbers of fish on a fishing-ground, say—there may be abundant statistical data. In such a problem we may find four leading experts, examining the evidence independently, arriving at four totally different conclusions. It follows, therefore, that in seeking reasons for the persistent survival of archaic types, we can but conjecture, and then in general terms only, with little hope of reaching any firm conclusions.

The survival of any individual animal must be dependent primarily upon an adequate supply of food and shelter, using the word "shelter" to include protection from the elements and from living enemies. The survival of a species is dependent upon the successful survival of the individuals comprising it. But, since individuals must sooner or later die, the perpetuation of a species depends also upon the successful reproduction of the individual. When we come to consider genera, that is, collections of species, or families, which are in turn collections of genera, more and more factors will come into operation. It follows from this that the larger the group we have to consider, the more numerous factors there will be to influence survival. Moreover, the less solid will be the basis for our speculations. For simplicity's sake, therefore, species rather than the larger groups will be considered here.

The influence of food may be felt in a variety of ways, by the quantity, the quality and the type of food taken. Generally speaking, animals may be approximately divided into carni-vores and herbivores, but not only are there different kinds of carnivores and of herbivores, but there are intermediate grades, as, for example, the omnivores, which will eat anything animal or vegetable. Provided we make the distinction between a carnivore, as normally understood, and an insectivore, it is noticeable that no living fossil is a pure carnivore, in the sense of being predatory on vertebrates and dependent upon killing speedy prey. Even in the marsupial fauna of Australia, which represents almost a living fossil fauna, carnivores like the thylacine, and possibly the Queensland wild cat (if it ever existed), have been the first to wilt under adverse circumstances. This is more readily understandable if we bear in mind the principle of food chains, or food pyramids. In any balanced biological unit, the herbivores are preyed upon by carnivores. The larger the carnivore the fewer the numbers the unit will support. In a given area, for example, there is a limit to the number of lions the populations of herbivorous big game can support without their numbers speedily falling off. Where a particular type of animal is thus "thin on the ground", it is the more susceptible to adverse circumstances. Also, although pure herbivores tend to exist in large numbers, they have the disadvantage of being vulnerable to the spread of endemic disease. An example is seen in the rinderpest which drastically reduced the herbivorous big game of Africa.

In between these two extremes are the omnivores, to which no food comes amiss. And the most successful omnivores seem to be those that take their food in the form of small particles, as animal and vegetable detritus. So long as a minimum of the flora and fauna remains, such animals are assured of a food supply, for, as long as there are animals and plants to die off, there will be decaying particles. Among such feeders we find *Lingula*, straining detritus from the sea, *Paranaspides*, living in a similar way in the freshwaters, the king-crab, sifting detritus from the mud. Cockroaches feeding on garbage and carrion, and silverfish feeding on starchy particles come very near to them.

There are, on the other hand, those like Peripatus and Tuatara that feed on insects and other small invertebrates, and are, therefore, carnivores, standing in the same relationship to their prey as, say, a cat to a mouse. These present an anomaly, and the best we can say is that they can use a wide range of food and are practically assured of a supply because their main prey, the insects, are so abundant. We can, in fact, sum up the question of food in the broad generalisation that a strictly carnivorous diet does not help survival (except where it involves feeding on insects or other invertebrates abundant in large numbers), and that survival seems to be associated mainly with a diet of food taken in a finely divided state.

Protection, or shelter, seems to follow much the same lines as food, in that there is no rule; we can do little more than generalise. Recalling the five lines of adaptive radiation, it looks as though the first to disappear is the cursorial, while the fossorial and aquatic lines offer the best chance of survival. Or, to put it in less formal terms, anything that keeps out of the way is likely to go unmolested, and so is more likely to survive. Thus, we have the mud-burrowing *Lingula*, the burrowing tuatara, peripatus sheltering under logs, the nocturnal kiwi and lungfishes in marshy places where, having lungs, they are able to exist under conditions which would be disadvantageous to predatory fishes due to the low oxygen-content of the water and the risk of desiccation. Probably, also, we can point to silverfish and springtails, both inconspicuous and keeping well to cover; and in their own way this applies also to the mountain shrimps and those that inhabit underground water. Platypus, too, lives in mountain streams and on islands. Apus has another advantage, of being able to inhabit temporary pools, giving it relative freedom from predators.

This retreat into inconspicuous or inaccessible habitats may have a greater importance for the survival of relics than appears at first sight, an argument that is supported by what takes place among certain races of human beings. Extensive study has shown that both human populations and those of many animal species follow very much the same trends although the factors affecting each of the species may be different. We are justified in assuming, therefore, that knowledge gained from studying the rise and fall of animal populations can be used to shed light on the same features of human populations, and vice versa. It is significant that the earlier human communities have retired before the spread of later communities into fastnesses similar to those occupied by the living fossils among animals. The island home of Australia has, for example, been the refuge of the aboriginal equally with the marsupials. The pygmy races have retired into dense primeval jungle, such as the Ituri Forest of Central Africa. The bushmen retired into the Kalahari Desert, the Ainu of Japan retreated on to the islands, and so on. The parallel is a very close one.

These human relict races and the living fossils among animals may also have another thing in common: that they lead solitary lives. It may be that they are thereby less prone to epidemic disease than the more markedly gregarious species. This isolation may, also, have a genetical significance, a point to which we shall return later.

In addition to the need for adequate food and shelter there is the desirability, from the point of view of the species, that the individual should be given a good start in life. So we may ask: Is there any reason to suppose that persistence of isolated types is linked with special advantages for the young? The incubation period of the two-foot tuatara, for example, is thirteen months, an unusually long period for any reptile. In lizards of about the same size as the tuatara it is usually from two to four months. Even for a large lizard, say, the Nile monitor, up to five feet long, it is only nine to ten months.

Generally speaking, the period of gestation, or incubation, as the case may be, tends to increase proportionately to the body size, and so does the longevity. As in all matters biological there is no rule, and such a statement can be no more than an approximation, more especially useful in comparing members of the same class. Therefore, when we find a two-foot reptile showing an unusually long period of incubation, and when this is linked with an unusual longevity, we are entitled to suppose that these things may have a significance. There are similar implications in the development of peripatus: in the viviparous species there is a long period of gestation. There is also a form of placental attachment of the embryo to the parent. Both these things recall the conditions found in the higher mammals. In the oviparous species of peripatus, the eggs are heavily yolked; which recalls the condition found, especially, in birds. Thus we find, in an archaic invertebrate, some of the conditions that have contributed significantly to the successful evolution of the highest vertebrates. The larval life of the king-crab suggests the same idea, although its implications are not so clear cut. The heavily yolked egg takes three weeks to hatch and the emerging larva carries a sufficient residue of the food-store to sustain it for the first month of its free life, which is reminiscent of what takes place in some of the more highly evolved fishes.

Usually, little is known of longevity, and complete details of the early development are not available for all living fossils, though in a sufficient number of them we know of some peculiarity giving advantages to the young. Thus, cockroaches carry their eggs about in a protective capsule; millipedes make a nest and show some degree of parental care; sharks lay large yolked eggs or are viviparous; scorpions carry their young on their backs in the early stages. The young of platypus have a prolonged stay in the nest, which suggests an extended parental care. It would take too much space to develop this theme, even if sufficient details were known upon which to base adequate conclusions. Enough has, however, been said to suggest that some form of protection for the young, or provision for the early period of their lives, may be an important contributory factor in the survival of living fossils.

On the face of it, we should assume that all living fossils persisting over long periods must either be comparatively tolerant to changes in the physical environment, or have evolved some special abilities to survive such changes. It would, however, be very difficult to prove this in any particular instance, since detailed information would be necessary not only in regard to the living animals but to their ancestors as well, which is clearly impossible. Estimations of the tolerance of an animal to physical changes involve detailed statistics of the temperature ranges, fluctuations in humidity, and the like, that it can endure, and, in the case of marine organisms, changes in salinity. On the other hand, an animal living below ground, even if only a few inches beneath the surface, and especially one that comes out only at night, will be living most of its time under fairly constant conditions of temperature and humidity. It could, therefore, be that the inconspicuous habits of so many living fossils bring, not only a comparative security from predators, but advantages in regard to physical conditions also. This alone would make for survival, whether or not there was a tolerance of extreme ranges of external conditions. Future knowledge of the Stephens Island frog, whose habitat has undergone such drastic changes, may tell us more about this.

As with extinction, so with survival we may be fairly sure that no single factor but a concatenation of favourable circumstances are necessary. A constant food supply, specific longevity, extended provision for the young, an inconspicuous habitat and the rest, all doubtless play their part. We have, however, to remember that there are different kinds of living fossils. There are the lone survivors, which have come down to the present time relatively unchanged, tuatara being the classic example of this. There are those represented by a few widely separated species which, again, have persisted relatively unchanged, such as peripatus, the lungfishes, king-crabs and the lamp-shell, *Lingula*. Then there are those which are represented by numerous species distributed all over the world, such as the silverfish, springtails and cockroaches, and to a lesser extent sharks, crocodiles and tortoises; these also are relatively unchanged. There is perhaps a fourth class, which includes relics, properly speaking, of flourishing groups that have undergone many changes and have died out leaving lone survivors; these are the camels, elephants, giraffes and okapi. Clearly, the combinations of factors responsible for survival must differ from one group to another, and each must be considered on its merits.

Extreme longevity in human beings cannot be ascribed to any one cause but to a combination of internal and external conditions which preserves life beyond the normal. And if we are justified in comparing the sequence of life in an individual with that of a species or group of species, then we must look in another direction for what is probably one of the main causes of prolonged existence in both, namely, the internal causes. And the most important of these is probably the genetical.

So far as we can see, long life in individual humans is hereditary. It tends to run in families. The basis of heredity is the gene, the ultra-microscopic catalyst which, carried in the germ-cell, determines form, behaviour and all other fundamentals of the life of an individual. Owing to the random or irregular sorting of the genes, the factors for heredity, contributed by each parent, no two members of a litter, brood or swarm are alike. Variation as seen in the offspring from one pair of parents is so much the greater as seen over the range of a species. In species comprising short-lived individuals—in butterflies, say—it is found that when successive generations are studied for a given locality or population, the outward appearance of the individuals differs slightly from year to year. Such slow fluctuating change could give rise in the process of time, and under certain conditions, to new species. More radical changes in the gene material can, however, give rise to quicker changes and to the more rapid evolution of species. It is not our purpose here to examine this problem further, but merely to emphasise the importance of the genes in influencing changes in races or species.

It is easy to see how, granted this mechanism for mixing and consequent change, species and genera could bud from a main stock, to produce a pattern comparable to the budding and growth of a tree. But while it helps us to visualise how, let us say, the twiggy growths arise, it does little to explain the long persistence of a single branch. There is, however, reason to believe that in certain organisms there is a resistance to the mixing of the genes, and, therefore, a resistance to change.

In a subject such as this, we are trying to encompass the complicated and minute details affecting a large number of animals distributed throughout the world and existing over vast periods of time. We have to choose, therefore, between engaging in lengthy explanations of a technical nature and trying to convey ideas in metaphors and similes. The first is, for practical reasons of space alone, impossible. The second method has its disadvantages, in that no one metaphor or simile alone suffices, and in using more than one there is apt to be conflict between them. The Tree of Descent is not wholly satisfactory; no more is the rocket idea, which tends to conflict with it. Neither dovetails smoothly with the genetical principles now briefly enunciated, yet each contributes something to the general picture, and their synthesis brings us somewhere near a true conception of the process of evolution, by which alone we can start to understand the significance of living fossils.

There is another side to this story of survival which is germane to our present discussion, and consideration of it helps to combine the various metaphors and similes and so to further our understanding of them. This relates to the varying rate of growth, development and progress of the parts of the body of any individual animal, and it is something we can best examine in our own bodies, for with these we are most familiar. We can start, for example, with the hand and the foot. We know that the basic architecture of the bones of the foot does not differ from that of the hand. Each comprises five digits, with each digit supported by four bones, except where, as in the thumb, the number is reduced to three. This pentadactyl (or five-fingered) plan, as it is called, is found in all vertebrates, in the feet of frogs, reptiles, apes and so on. It can be readily traced, in a modified form, in the wing of a bat or a bird, even in the leg of a horse or the flipper of a whale, where there has been extreme modification. The pure pentadactyl condition, as we see it in some frogs and lizards, can be taken to represent, therefore, the basic or original plan. It is spoken of as gener-alised. Arguing from this, we should suppose that at some point in the ancestral human stock, hand and foot did not differ markedly, as indeed is the case in certain monkeys. In present-day man, however, the foot has undergone considerable change and is now specialised, for walking, and for little else. The hand is still generalised; it is an all-purpose organ, little changed from the original—and, therefore, partaking of the quality of a living fossil.

It is not always so easy to make comparisons of this kind in the realm of human structure, and it would be pointless here to try to examine every feature of the human body in this way, both because it would take too long and because it would carry the analogy too far. We can, however, profitably take a few more examples. One of the more obvious features is the hair covering the body. Except for a few places, such as the soles of the feet and the palms of the hands, our bodies are clothed with hair. This is more obvious in some persons than in others, but in all it is present. Moreover, there is good reason to suppose that at an earlier period in the history of the human race, this covering of hair was more pronounced than it is today, and covered more abundantly every part of the body. Now it is most thick on the head, with a few pronounced patches else-where. The reduction in this hairy coat, that once (it is pre-sumed) covered the whole body, to what is mainly a head covering, may, at a stretch, be compared with the distribution of, say, the lungfishes, which at one time seem to have ranged over the whole world and are now limited mainly to Central Africa, with two outliers, Australia and South America. On the strength of this analogy, then, hair on the human body can be regarded in the nature of a relic, or living fossil. It is not without significance that we find artists, attempting to portray the man of the future, frequently showing him with a hairless head. This may be mere coincidence, or it may be an intuitive recognition that this "living fossil" in human structure must one day disappear.

Other "living fossils"—relics is perhaps the better term in this connection—are seen in the finger-nails, the appendix, the tonsils and a number of other less familiar or less obvious features. According to the comparative anatomist, these are organs which have fallen into desuetude, or, to use more homely language, are on the way out. Some are completely vestigial; others may have changed their function; and others, like the body-covering of hair, have merely become restricted in distribution. The first category of these relict organs is paralleled among animal species by tuatara or Stephens Island frog. The third has already been compared with the lungfishes. The second category, in which there has been a change of function, is difficult to homologise with animal species, but could be represented by the coelacanths which were at first freshwater creatures, later inhabitants of the shallow seas, and still later found living in deep seas—a change of function, in a sense (from freshwater to marine), with little change in form.

Emphasis has been laid, from time to time during the course of preceding chapters, on the comparison that can be drawn between the lives of individuals and those of species and other higher groups. The only reason for seeking to extend these analogies to organs of the body is this, that if the comparison holds good for them, then the fact that we know the destiny of individual organs to be influenced largely by genetical factors suggests that the destiny of species, genera, families and the rest are similarly governed. It has already been suggested that, accident and misadventure excepted, longevity in human beings is hereditary, or genetical. So presumably the survival of species and other higher groupings of organisms are similarly influenced. Whether a species shall have large-yolked eggs, placental attachments of the embryo, shall show parental care, or have a low metabolic rate, is dependent upon genetical changes. Coupled with such changes, it would appear that there are other genetical factors which inhibit or resist changes in other directions. Essentially, therefore, a living fossil is not merely an organism, animal or plant which has survived, but one which in its gross features has suffered relatively little change, while other less obvious parts, those in fact which are not usually preserved in fossils, may have altered, but always in the direction of giving advantages for survival. These, then, are the internal changes. The living fossil is also an organism that has survived the outward changes because its line has enjoyed a sufficient supply of food, freedom from overwhelming enemies or competitors, and has not had to meet catastrophic changes of geography or climate; or one that, if it has had to meet these, has been able either to escape to an isolated or inconspicuous haven, or by reason of its internal vitality has been able to make good its losses and regain its former abundance and range.

CHAPTER XVI

MONSTERS AND MYSTERY ANIMALS

EVERY age and every continent has had its stories of mysterious animals. Some seem to have been figments of the imagination, others due to misconceptions about real animals; and even in these days, when exploration, discovery and research have quartered and encircled the globe, there still remains a hard core of unexplained mysteries. Outstanding cases of this kind are the marsupial wild cat and giant kangaroo, of Australia; the abominable snowman, of Asia; the nandi bear, of Africa; the tatzelwurm and the Loch Ness monster, in Europe; the tail-less ape, of South America; the ogo-pogo, of North America; and the sea-serpent.

There is not the space, nor is it desirable to discuss all these fully here; but because there is a sustained expectation that one or other of these, or, indeed, some others not yet named, may at any moment make headlines, some reference to them is imperative. It is the more necessary since partial belief in them is usually coupled with the idea, or the direct suggestion, that we have to do with survivors of bygone times; or, in other words, with something that either is, or flavours of, a living fossil. The discovery of the Coelacanth fish, when the scientific world believed every member of its order to have died out not less than 70 million years ago, seems to make almost anything possible. Is there any likelihood of some new large animal hitherto unknown to science coming to light in the future?

Every year the pages of the scientific journals throughout the world contain descriptions of hundreds of new species, but these are mainly small or medium-sized animals, and, for the most part, they are invertebrates from land or sea, or else are

256

marine vertebrates. Some show archaic characters, a few may come very near to being living fossils, but, as a rule, none of these is sufficiently out of the ordinary to cause a stir in scientific circles, least of all among the lay public. If the truth be told, those scientists whose task it is to describe and catalogue new species of animals tend to grow somewhat weary of a seemingly never-ending task. They also tend to be very sceptical of the chances of spectacular finds of larger animals. It is salutary, therefore, to consider for a moment how comparatively recent are the discoveries of some of the large or medium-sized mammals, many of which are now household words, and the dates on which the animals themselves were made known to science (although some were reported much earlier).

The aye-aye, of Madagascar, was first reported in 1780 and not seen again until 1860. *Plagiodontia aedium* (a rodent), of San Domingo, was first recorded in 1836, and not seen again until 1948. Marco Polo's sheep was first seen by the great traveller after whom it has been named, but it was not made known to science until 1838. The golden hamster, of which one specimen was seen in Syria in 1839, was not rediscovered until 1930. The gorilla, Père David's deer and the giant panda, first discovered in 1847, 1866 and 1869 respectively; the gerenuk, known to the ancient Egyptians, but not to science until 1878; the okapi (1901), the giant forest hog (1904), both of Central Africa, the mountain nyala, of Abyssinia (1908), the golden takin, of Western China (1910), and *Osbornictus piscivora*, of Central Africa (1919), were all large enough to be seen yet escaped detection until this century or last. Finally, *Plagiodontia hylaeum*, also of San Domingo, was not made known to science until as recently as 1948.

Two other mammals deserve mention. The Victorian genet, of the Ituri Forest, is practically unknown except for skins collected by natives. And Schomburghk's deer has never been seen in the wild by Europeans. Probably nothing would have been known of it, apart from the random records of its suspected presence by licensed surveyors, police magistrates and the like, had not the antlers, in velvet, been prized for their alleged medicinal value. As it is, although the antlers have appeared as an article of commerce in the Siamese markets, only one complete and mounted specimen is known.

We are reaching finality, however, in some groups. For example, the discovery of a species of bird new to science is regarded as quite exceptional nowadays. We are nearing this situation so far as mammals are concerned. The large reptiles have been fairly fully catalogued, and the amphibia offer few opportunities for surprises.

There are three main areas of the world from which surprises in the shape of large land animals cannot be ruled out. These are the jungles of Matto Grosso, in South America, associated in our memories with the disappearance of Colonel Fawcett, in his search for a lost world; the tropical rain forests of Central Africa; and large areas of Central Asia. While these remain incompletely explored there is always the possibility of some/ thing new being brought to light. As for the seas, which have yielded us in recent years the Coelacanth, they constitute such a vast mass, in depth and extent, that we can claim to have done no more than take a sample of their inhabitants.

The Bhanjakris, or Abominable Snowman, is the best/ documented of the mysteries mentioned in our list. So far as the western world is concerned, it was first recorded in 1899 by a mountaineer who claimed to have seen, at a height of 18,500 feet on Kanchenjunga, a peak in the Himalayas near Mount Everest, a long trail of large footprints in the snow. The 1923 Everest Expedition saw an unidentified object moving far above the snowline, and later found footprints in the snow at 20,000 feet. Shipton found similar prints at 16,000 feet in 1936, and in 1951, and again in 1952 brought home photo/ graphs of these prints. So much for the solid evidence. The belief in the Abominable Snowman is held by the natives over a wide area of Tibet, Nepal, Sikkim and Bhutan. There have been reports of terrifying roars, and according to some native reports the Snowman is powerfully built, with arms reaching to the knees and the body covered with long dark hair. It is said to be capable of uprooting trees and pitching boulders with ease. There have also been unsubstantiated reports of the Snowman having been taken captive.

Zoologists who have ventured an opinion after examining photographs of the footprints have suggested that they were made either by a large bear or a langur. Such opinions have been given tentatively and have been received with a thinly veiled scepticism by fellow zoologists and informed laymen alike. The objections to their acceptance are twofold. In the first place, it is highly questionable whether a large beast would be able to exist at such inhospitable heights. The second problem is presented by the tracks themselves. They consist of large prints forming a single trail, each print in front of the last, of a size and disposition such as might be made by a bipedal elephant taking large strides.

It is always possible that a quite prosaic explanation may eventually be found for the Snowman. Large mammals are known to wander up mountains well beyond their normal habitat. There is the case of the leopard that climbed to the top of Mount Kilimanjaro, its body having later been found there preserved in ice. I have letters from people who have seen bear tracks in the snow going straight up a mountain and down the other side; others have seen a large monkey sitting on the peak of a mountain, apparently doing nothing more than admiring the view. On one occasion I was given a verbal description of a large old bear that had lost most of its toes from frostbite, whose trails could not have been construed had the beast itself not been shot to reveal the reason for the abnormal tracks. This goes to show that the so-called mystery animal may, in many cases, prove to be an ordinary, indeed a well-known, animal behaving abnormally, or suffering some abnormality of shape or size.

Another series of animals, known very largely by their tracks, belong to Africa. These are the nandi bear, or chimiset, the nunda, the lau, the pterodactyl and the chipekwe. It would not be possible to deal with all the accounts of these, which in any case are set forth by Frank W. Lane in *Nature Parade*. For the nandi bear there are reports of footprints "four times as big as a man's"; they show the imprint of three clawed toes, made, it is presumed, by an arboreal and nocturnal animal having something of the appearance of a bear, with the fore- quarters and legs covered with a long soft fur, in height about four feet six at the shoulders, with the body sloping away to the hindquarters. Accounts differ slightly, but all testify to the evident terror inspired in the natives by the sight of the beast's tracks and by its terrifying roar. There is the testimony, too, of a number of white explorers, including Selous, the greatest of all African hunters. The Nandi Expedition of 1905 reported seeing on the Uasin Gishu Plateau something sitting on its haunches at a range of not more than thirty yards, which dropped forward and shambled off before they could observe it further. Captain R. C. S. Pitman, while he does not believe in the nandi bear, says in *A Game Warden Among his Charges*: "There have been innumerable reports of strange creatures from the Uasin Gishu and Trans-Nzoia districts. . . . Not long ago there was scarcely a white man in those districts who had not at one time or another either actually seen the beast or had some experience connected with it."

The general view of zoologists seems to be that the nandi bear is an old male hyena, but Captain Pitman writes: "Anyone who has lived in a 'Nandi bear atmosphere' cannot doubt the reality of the dread the brute inspires." And Frank Lane comments: ". . . it is well to remember that the natives who draw and describe strange beasts not yet recognised by science are the same people who also drew and described the okapi and other little-known creatures before they, too, were officially recognised by professional zoologists". A compara- tively recent example of the natives proving right in the face of European scepticism was in the case of the king cheetah. R. I. Pocock commented on this discovery: ". . . most extra- ordinary that so large and distinct a species should remain for so long unknown". Although the king cheetah is now regarded as an occasional mutant of the ordinary cheetah, the significance of its discovery is not thereby lessened.

The nunda is equally elusive, and, like the nandi bear, its existence is testified by native and white alike. It has been described as "a gigantic brindled cat . . . not a lion nor a leopard, but a huge cat as big as a donkey and marked like a tabby" that inflicts terrible maulings and is capable of carrying off a boy, leaving a spoor like that of a leopard but as large as that of the largest lion. The tabby markings and the brindled hair seem to be a common feature of most of the reports, as does the donkey-size, and there are several instances in which hair has been said to be left behind, gripped in the hands of its victims.

The lau has been reported by native Africans and also by officers of the Victoria Nyanza steamers, and explorers of standing have testified to having seen it. It is described as from forty to one hundred feet long, with a long neck, a snake-like head and large tentacles. Its home is in Lake Victoria. It has been described as brown or dark yellow in colour, with the body as thick as that of a horse. Descriptions such as this leave too much to the imagination and could never be accepted as positive evidence. At the same time, this does not rule out the possibility of some large aquatic animal being brought to light subsequently. Another mystery animal has been reported from the swampy forests of Central Africa. Captain Pitman refers to the native fear of a gigantic bat-bird, to look upon which means death. He asks the obvious question: Whence does the African who could never have heard tell of the pterodactyl derive such a fanciful idea if there were nothing to support it? Ivan Sanderson, in *Animal Treasure*, recounts how he actually saw the flying monster. Bathing in a river at dusk, he was suddenly warned by shouts from his companions on the bank:

I looked. Then I let out a shout also and instantly bobbed down under the water, because, coming straight at me only a few feet above the water was a black thing the size of an eagle. I had only a glimpse of its face, yet that was sufficient, for its lower jaw hung open and bore a semicircle of pointed white teeth about their own width apart from each other. Just before it became too dark to see, it came again, hurtling back down the river, its teeth chattering, the air "shss-shssing" as it was cleft by the great dracula-like wings.

For the description of the chipekwe, we must turn to Carl Hagenbeck, the German animal collector, who received reports from the interior of Rhodesia, both from his own travellers and from an English big-game hunter. In all cases, however, these men had had their reports from natives, of a monster, half-elephant, half-dragon, living in the swamps that stretched for hundreds of miles. "As the stories came from so many different sources, and all tend to substantiate each other I am almost convinced that some such reptile must still be in existence." Hagenbeck, who wrote these words, was sufficiently sure of the continued existence of some dinosaur of the brontosaurus type that he equipped an expedition to find it, but one after another the members of the expedition went down with fever and the venture was finally abandoned. According to J. E. Hughes, author of *Eighteen Years on Lake Bangweulu*, there was a traditional story among the natives of the killing of such a monster in Lake Bangweulu, and he gives it as his opinion that the creature is now extinct although only recently so. Again, there is little enough description of the beast, but there are said to be drawings of it on the walls of certain caves in Central Africa.

The ogo-pogo, of North America, seems to be in the same class as the sea-serpent or the Loch Ness Monster, while the tatzelwurm of Central Europe, although living on land, is equally elusive. The latter is described as a small animal with short legs that lives in crevices in the rocks in the Alps. It is said to leap out and bite its victim, but apparently no more than a fleeting glimpse is obtained of it before it darts back again. There is at least one account of a man who declared he had been attacked by a tatzelwurm and who died in hospital of an unknown poison.

One of the best documented of these mysterious animals, apart from the sea-serpent, is, however, the Queensland tiger-cat. The first published record appears to have been communi-cated to a meeting of the Zoological Society of London in 1871 and published in the Proceedings for that year (pages 629–630).

Mr. Sclater called the attention of the meeting to the reported existence in Northern Queensland of an undescribed animal of about the size of a Dingo (*Canis dingo*), of which no specimen had yet been obtained by naturalists. In reply to some inquiries on this subject lately addressed to Mr. Brinsley G. Sheridan, Police Magistrate of Cardwell, Rockingham Bay, Queensland, Mr. Sclater has received the following letter, dated 2nd August, 1871:

Sir.—I fear you must have misunderstood Mr. Arthur Scott about my son having been attacked by some unknown ferocious animal in the bush. It was simply this. One evening, strolling along a path close to the shore of Rockingham Bay, a small terrier, my son's companion, took a scent up from a piece of scrub near the beach, and followed, barking furiously, towards the coast-range westwards. My boy (thirteen years of age, but an old bushman, who would put half those described in novels to the blush) followed and found in the long grass, about half a mile from the spot where the scent was first taken up, an animal described by himself as follows: "It was lying camped in the long grass and was as big as a native Dog; its face was round like that of a Cat, it had a long tail, and its body was striped from the ribs under the belly with yellow and black. My Dog flew at it, but it could throw him. When they were together I fired my pistol at its head; the blood came. The animal then ran up a leaning tree, and the Dog barked at it. It then got savage and rushed down the tree at the Dog and then at me. I got frightened and came home."

It was just dark when the boy came home in a high

state of excitement and told me the story. From inquiry I find that this is not the first time a similar animal has been seen in this neighbourhood. Tracks of a sort of Tiger have been seen in Dalrymple's Gap by people camping there, and Mr. Reginald Uhr, now Police Magistrate at St. George's, whilst one of the native mounted police officers in this district, saw the same animal my son describes. The country is so sparsely populated, and the jungles (or as we call them here, "scrubs") so dense and so little known, that I have no doubt that animals of this kind exist in considerable numbers, the abundance of food and their timidity preventing our more intimate knowledge of their habits. I shall be most happy to send you, should it be my good fortune to drop across one of them, its skin and skeleton. I only regretted, as my poor boy did, that he had not my revolver, as he says he stood, when it was fighting with the Dog, at less than a yard from the animal.

The following year (*see* Proc. Zool. Soc. London, 1872, page 355) Gould read an extract from a letter addressed to the Secretary by Mr. Walter T. Scott, C.M.Z.S., dated Vale of Herbert, Cardwell, Queensland, 4th December, 1871. Mr. Scott wrote as follows of the supposed "Native Tiger" of Queensland, concerning which Mr. Sclater had previously communicated the evidence given by Mr. Sheridan (*see* P.Z.S., 1871, page 629):

As to the Tiger, I am inclined to think there really is some large carnivorous animal as yet undescribed in this neighbourhood. A Mr. Hull, Licensed Surveyor, was lately at work with a party of five men, surveying on the Murray and Mackay rivers, north of Cardwell. They were lying in their tents one night between eight and nine o'clock when they were all startled by a loud roar close to the tents. They seized their guns and carefully reconnoitred; but the animal had departed. In the morning they found the tracks of the unknown visitor, of which Mr. Hull took the measurements and a rough sketch. I send you part of a leaf of Mr. Hull's field-book, containing the original sketch—and also his

83. RECONSTRUCTION OF THE QUEENSLAND TIGER-
CAT based on eye-witness' reports, of an animal which
may or may not exist.

drawing of the track, of the natural size. Mr. Hull assures
me that the drawing was a very faithful one, the soft ground
having taken the impression with all its details. I have also
examined some of the men who were with Mr. Hull. They
all tell the same story, and say they heard the animal three
nights in succession.

I think that I have already mentioned to you that a bullock-
driver of ours, as long ago as 1864, came in one day with a
story that he had seen a Tiger; but as he was a notorious liar
we did not believe a word of it at the time. Yet it is possible
he may really have seen the same animal, which must, I
think, from its claws, be allied to the Tasmanian Thylacine
(*Thylacinus cynocephalus*).

Troughton, in his *Furred Animals of Australia* (1946), lists
other testimony, as follows, but gives no references, so that one
can but quote his words. George Sharp, a well-known
naturalist-collector, had a passing sight of something "larger

and darker than the Tasmanian Tiger, with the stripes showing very distinctly". It vanished before he could raise his gun. A more detailed description comes from Ion L. Idriess.

Up here in York Peninsula we have a tiger-cat that stands as high as a hefty, medium-sized dog. His body is lithe and sleek and beautifully striped in black and grey. His pads are armed with lance-like claws of great tearing strength. His ears are sharp and pricked, and his head is shaped like that of a tiger. My introduction to this beauty was one day when I heard a series of snarls from the long buffalo-grass skirting a swamp. On peering through the grass I saw a full-grown kangaroo, backed up against a tree, the flesh of one leg torn clear from the bone. A streak of black and grey shot towards the "roo's" throat, then seemed to twist in the air, and the kangaroo slid to earth with the entrails literally torn out. In my surprise I incautiously rustled the grass, and the great cat ceased the warm feast that he had promptly started upon, stood perfectly still over his victim, and for ten seconds returned me gaze for gaze. Then the skin wrinkled back from the nostrils, white fangs gleamed and a low growl issued from his throat. I went backwards and lost no time in getting out of the entangling grass. The next brute I saw was dead, and beside him was my much-prized staghound, also dead. This dog had been trained from puppyhood in tackling wild boars, and his strength and courage were known by all the prospectors over the country. The cat had come fossicking round my camp on the Alice River.

Troughton's final account is from the *Brisbane Courier* (date not given), communicated by G. de Tournoeur, who in company with P. B. Scougall was riding from Munna Creek towards Tiaro township. Their horses shied and they dismounted, to see a large "cat", twenty yards away, astride a dead calf, glaring defiance and emitting a growling whine. It was dusk and raining, but they judged the beast's size to be that of a mastiff. It was "a dirty fawn colour, with a whitish belly and broad blackish tiger stripes. The head was round with rather prominent lynx-like ears", a tail reaching to the ground and large pads.

In his own book Troughton comments: "The creature probably lives in the thick forests which man seldom penetrates, or in which he makes so much noise in getting through that the more wary animal is seldom seen." And again, ". . . there seems no doubt that a large striped marsupial-cat haunts the tangled forests of North Queensland".

It is possible that nothing more may be heard of the alleged "tiger-cat"; that it may go down, or has gone down, before human settlement, or in competition with the wild dog, and is now extinct. In any case, to the zoologist, with no more evidence of its existence than that to hand, any discussion on the possibility of such a beast having formed part of the Australian fauna is somewhat academic. It is, however, not without profit to examine the arguments for and against the testimony of eye-witnesses.

The first obvious comparison is with the thylacine. It is significant that all reports of the "tiger-cat" suggest a likeness to it. There are, however, differences which would seem to preclude the eye-witnesses having been deceived by the actual presence of the thylacine in Northern Queensland, or having been influenced by a knowledge, however remote, of the appearance of that animal. The only drawing of its track could not have been that of a thylacine, unless it is a woefully bad representation of the track as seen. On the other hand, a strong argument against the existence of the "cat" is that, whereas traces of the thylacine have been found sub-fossil, none has been seen of the "tiger-cat".

It is, however, worth drawing attention to the attempts in recent years to locate the thylacine, which is known to exist. David Fleay (Vict. Nat. Melbourne, 63, 1946, pages 129, 154, 174) has described his persistent and well-organised attempts to see or trap the thylacine, which failed completely. Yet he is able to include at the end of his account the news that tracks were subsequently seen by other people. This merely means, as any field naturalist is aware, that it is possible to search diligently and for a long time the territory of a known species, and yet never obtain a sight of it. There are plenty of places in England, for example, where badgers are plentiful yet the local inhabitants are unaware of it. Moreover, a visiting naturalist may try for a long time without success to have a sight of them. Yet in these same localities motorists often report seeing badgers in their headlights. If for motorists with headlights we read a police magistrate, a police magistrate's son, a licensed surveyor and others, and for heavily settled England we read Queens, land, with a scanty population and forests little explored, it is not surprising if no zoologist has seen a "tiger-cat" and no camera has recorded it. It is merely another instance of random observation giving the only chance of success.

Before leaving the comparison with the thylacine, there is yet one other, more convincing, argument to put forward. Comparing the marsupial fauna of Australia with the placental mammals in other parts of the world, there is a strong parallel between their ecological grouping. In both there are grazing, browsing, arboreal, burrowing and the many other types necessary to a balanced ecology. Among the marsupials predators are represented by the thylacine, which is the counter, part of the wolf, and a few smaller animals are also present, but the counterpart of the big cats is missing. Theoretically there must have existed in pre-settled Australia the ecological niche for a tiger-cat.

It must appear remarkable to the non-zoologist that such a well-documented animal should be the subject of such intense scepticism, even allowing that we possess no material evidence of its existence in the shape of a few bones, a piece of the skin, or even a tuft of its hair. Unfortunately, it has happened all too often that an apparently authentic account of some strange creature has been proved to relate to something ordinary or well known as soon as some part of the animal has been made available for examination. It is no reflection on the integrity of a witness, such fallibility is human and something to which everyone is prone at some time or another. Those with field experience in so prosaic and sophisticated a countryside as our own know the trick light can play, how deceptive can be the matter of size, and the apparent distortions resulting from a fleeting glimpse of an otherwise familiar and commonplace animal. Where the emotions arising from fear or solitude are also operating, such illusions and deceptions would tend to be enhanced. Added to this, very few people are competent observers unless there has been something in their training to make them otherwise. Finally, there is such a thing as subjective observation, the phenomenon, which is wholly unconscious, of seeing what the mind wishes one to see.

Even when all these things are allowed for, there are still a number of other factors which may account for some at least of the extraordinary reports. To begin with, there is always a percentage, admittedly small, of individuals in every species which grow to an unusually large size. I have shown else-where* that if the average height of a male Londoner be taken as 5 ft. 8 in., then an unusually tall man would be one 6 ft. 4 in. high, but the record height is 9 ft. 3 in. If we take the various species of mammals for which reliable measurements are available, we find that the outsizes for the species are: 68 per cent above average size, and 40 per cent above the unusually large. Such abnormally large individuals of already large species could readily deceive, especially in certain lights.

Another factor involves the possibility of freak colouring, as in the so-called king cheetah, or even freak shapes. Then there is the chance of freak behaviour, or even normal be-haviour of which we are ignorant, an example of which will be given in connection with the conger eel. It needs only large size, trick of light, abnormal colour and freak behaviour, with a little faulty observation and some subjective thinking, or a combination of some of these, and a monster is born in which the eye-witness believes implicitly.

* See *Illustrated London News*, March 8, 1952.

Finally, of course, there is always the possibility that one or other of the alleged monsters may in fact exist!

The kind of freak behaviour referred to above is seen in the following account of the conger eel. Let me add that, appearances to the contrary, it is not the purpose here to argue either in favour of, or against, the sea-serpent or the Loch Ness Monster but to show how a natural phenomenon could give rise to exaggerated stories.

It is thirty years now since I first became interested in stories of the sea-serpent and during that time I have neglected no opportunity of discussing the subject, either with believers or disbelievers. The former are more numerous than is commonly supposed, and can be divided into two categories: those who, on an ocean voyage, have seen something which they can only ascribe to some unknown animal of giant size; and those who, having examined the evidence, find it credible, but for fear of ridicule prefer to maintain a discreet silence. The evidence includes a welter of optical illusions, practical jokes, hoaxes and imperfect observations, yet, when all these are dismissed, there remains a hard core of detailed descriptions by competent observers which cannot be lightly put aside. There is another striking thing: that the evidence for both the sea-serpent and the Loch Ness Monster is remarkably similar in all particulars. Both refer to a moving object—a living beast presumably—of considerable length, moving at speed, and remaining at the surface for a short time only, during which the most distinctive feature is a series of humps showing above the water-line.

There is nothing in the more reliable stories that is beyond belief except those humps. They form the big obstacle for the zoologist, who rightly points out that it is highly unlikely that a beast of such dimensions could produce the vertical undulations in its spine necessary to give this effect.

Some years ago, while pondering this problem more intently than usual, I came to the conclusion that giant eels were probably responsible for all the stories about sea-serpents and the Loch Ness Monster. They are the only known animals

equally at home in salt or brackish water—or even fresh water
in some cases—that are sufficiently amphibious to be able to
keep the head out of water for the length of time required by
the various reports, and which habitually lurk at the bottom,
making only infrequent and sporadic appearances at the
surface. Within recent years, eel larvae 3 ft. or more in length
have been discovered in the sea. The larva of our common
freshwater eel is 3 in. long, and grows into an adult 3 ft. or
more in length. It is a matter of simple arithmetic that, if the
proportions are preserved, a 3 ft. larva could grow into an
adult 36 ft. or more long. Size, then, is no obstacle to the
acceptance of these persistent stories; nor speed, as anyone will
know who has watched a conger swim. Only the humps
remain, the sole obstacle to acceptance.

It was when reviewing these things, then, that it appeared
worth my while to assume that the stories of the sea-serpent
and the monster might be true; and, starting, from this premise,
to see if the problem of the humps could be solved. If, for
example, eels ever swim at the surface and on their sides, the
appearance of a series of humps could be expected. Accord-
ingly, I got into touch with as many angler friends as possible,
to see if any one of them had seen an eel swimming in this way.
None could recall seeing an eel at the surface.

It happened that a little later I was making a commentary
for a film of life under the sea. It was on a Saturday afternoon
towards the end of this task, while watching a piece of the film
that I had seen again and again, a scene of a conger swimming
over the bottom of the sea. Then something suddenly struck
me, and I asked for this portion to be run through again. The
conger was swimming at speed, on its side, the body undulating
as it slid over the rocks, an inch or two above them.

As soon as possible I went to the Aquarium at the London
Zoo—choosing the Monday, when there would be few
visitors—and stationed myself before the large tank containing
the conger eels. In the tank were half a dozen eels, the longest
some 5 ft. in length. For half an hour nothing happened,

except that one smallish conger, with its head thrust in a crevice in the rock, leisurely twisted the hinder half of its body into the horizontal position and slowly undulated just that part of it. A little later, a larger eel that had, up till then, been lying on its back, periodically yawning, rose bodily in the water, until a foot or so off the bottom, turned on its side and vigorously undulated its body, the waves passing along the body producing a series of humps from head to tail. It was all over in seconds and the eel sank languidly to the bottom, turned on its back and resumed its yawning.

During the next half-hour, several queer things happened. One of the smaller eels, $2\frac{1}{2}$ ft. long, rose from the bottom of the tank and gently tilted its body until it was suspended in mid-water head down. Then it glided to the surface until 9 in. of its tail protruded vertically above the water, in which position it swam gently along. A larger eel doing this, with 6 ft. of its tail erect above the surface of the sea, would produce an appearance difficult to interpret, or to have believed.

Several such things occurred, but the most important thing was still to come. As I was about to turn away, a 5 ft. conger, hitherto quiescent in a drain-pipe lying on the bottom of the tank, emerged and swam slowly and effortlessly around at about mid-water for about ten minutes. Then it suddenly rose to the surface, turned on its side, and undulated its body violently, causing a flurry of water and a series of humps above the water-line. Then it slowly sank to the bottom into the drain-pipe and settled down once more to rest. Meanwhile, the surface of the water, left in violent agitation, slowly subsided. A really large eel carrying out such a manœuvre would give a picture of the sea-serpent.

It may be that there are "monsters" on the land or in the sea whose presence has yet to be revealed. It could happen that further living fossils—relics of a lost world—may yet come to light: the finding in recent years of the living coelacanth fish has made almost anything possible. The greater probability is, however, that monsters and mysteries belong in reality to the world of the commonplace, or nearly so, that they are known animals seen in a different light and inadequately observed. At all events, the story of living fossils, while it may have its moments of drama, is compounded of the prosaic, often humble, survivor subjected to painstaking and objective research.

INDEX

L.F.—19